JEWELS

The Story of the Founding of Alpha Phi Alpha Fraternity
(Second Edition)
#The Alpha Hashtag History Project

Darrius Jerome Gourdine

DJG
Enterprises

Cover Photography: James Ravenell Photography

Cover design by Jossan Robinson, Design1320, LLC. ®

Back Cover Headshot Photography: James McDuff

Casting by Phil John

For speaking engagements, send inquiries to: darrius@jewels1906.com.

www.jewels1906.com

 ISBN 0-9755660-0-8

Second Edition printing

THE ALPHA
#HASHTAG HISTORY
PROJECT

The Alpha Hashtag History Project

In this Second Edition of *Jewels: The Story of the Founding of Alpha Phi Alpha Fraternity*, I had a desire to add more to the book. I didn't want to add or take away from the story itself but I wanted to add an element of Alpha history and social media. I came up with the Alpha Hashtag History Project. At the top of each page of this book you will see a hashtag. Every hashtag is different. Each one is for an individual chapter of Alpha Phi Alpha Fraternity, Incorporated. They are randomly selected and in no particular order. Each hashtag is linked to a particular history fact that is not commonly known about that chapter. All of the hashtags can be found by using either Facebook, Twitter or Instagram. By typing in the hashtag in either of the 3 social media platforms, you will see the history fact and have the ability to comment as well.

I wish to thank all of the brothers who contributed historical information about their chapters when I inquired. I especially wish to thank Brother Donald Ross who supplied me with a ton of information for a number of chapters.

To join the Alpha Hashtag History Project page on Facebook, visit www.facebook.com/groups/alphahashtag and request to be added. You will be added and can then see all of the historical hashtag images. To see the Alpha Hashtag History Project on Twitter, search for each hashtag individually by typing in the full hashtag name. You will then see each historical hashtag image.

Follow on Instagram @alphahashtag

Dedication

This book is dedicated to our past. To the Founders who exercised tremendous tenacity, forethought and vision. We thank each of them for the spirit of unity which they obediently followed in creating both brotherhood and sisterhood vehicles for our people:

Jewel Henry Arthur Callis, Jewel Charles Henry Chapman, Jewel Eugene Kinkle Jones, Jewel George Biddle Kelley, Jewel Nathaniel Allison Murray, Jewel Robert Harold Ogle, Jewel Vertner Woodson Tandy, Ethel Hedgeman Lyle, Beulah E. Burke, Lillie Burke, Margaret Flagg Holmes, Marjorie Hill, Lucy Diggs Slowe, Marie Woolfolk Taylor, Anna Easter Brown, Lavinia Norman, Elder Watson Diggs, Dr. Byron K. Armstrong, Dr. Guy L. Grant, Ezra D. Alexander, Edward G. Irvin, Paul W. Caine, Dr. Marcus P. Blakemore, Attorney Henry T. Asher, John Milton Lee, George Edmonds, Edgar Love, Frank Coleman, Oscar Cooper, Ernest E. Just, Osceola Macarthy Adams, Marguerite Young Alexander, Winona Cargile Alexander, Ethel Cuff Black, Bertha Pitts Campbell, Zephyr Chisom Carter, Edna Brown Coleman, Jessie McGuire Dent, Frederica Chase Dodd, Myra Davis Hemmings, Olive C. Jones, Jimmie Bugg Middleton, Pauline Oberdorfer Minor, Vashti Talor Murphy, Naomi Sewell Richardson, Mamie Redy Rose, Eliza P. Shippen, Florence Letcher Toms, Ethel Carr Watson, Wertie Blackwell Weaver, Madree Penn White, Edith Motte Young, The Honorable A. Langston Taylor, The Honorable Leonard F. Morse, The Honorable Charles I. Brown, Viola Tyler, Pearl Neal, Fannie Pettie, Myrtle Tyler, Arizona Cleaver Stemons, Pearl Anna Neal, Fannie Pettie Watts, Myrtle Tyler Faithful, Viola Tyler Goings, The Most Honorable Deceased Pearl Mary Lou Allison Little, The Most Honorable Deceased Pearl Dorothy Haney Whiteside, The Most Honorable Deceased Pearl Vivian White Marbury, The Most Honorable Deceased Pearl Nannie Mae Gahn Johnson, The Most Honorable Deceased Pearl Hattie Mae Dulin Redford, The Most Honorable Deceased Pearl Bessie M. Downey Martin, The Most Honorable Deceased Pearl Cubena McClure, Albert Hicks, Lonnie Spruill Jr., Charles Briscoe, Frank Coakley, John Slade, Baron Willis, Webster, Charles Brown, Louis Hudnell, Charles Gregory, Elias Dorsey Jr, and Michael Williams.

The Seven Jewels of Alpha Phi Alpha Fraternity, Incorporated

Jewels Henry Arthur Callis

Jewel Charles Henry Chapman

Jewel Eugene Kinckle Jones

Jewel George Biddle Kelley

Jewel Nathaniel Allison Murray

Jewel Robert Harold Ogle

Jewel Vertner Woodson Tandy

"Our Founders knew scholastic achievement was the key to developing a life of purpose. They encouraged social change through service and action. They were determined to inspire a generation of men to invest in themselves and make a difference. Today, every Alpha man is asked to make an investment in his fraternity and his community. We are asked to invest in the continuing evolution of all brothers by working together for the better making of men and for the betterment of our communities. This edition showcases that Alpha Phi Alpha has evolved while maintaining its core foundation. Brother Gourdine is inspired to tell the story of challenges and triumphs through the eyes of his brothers. We are expecting his narrative to inspire the next generation of young men to make solid contributions to society, and one day to Alpha Phi Alpha. Congratulations Brother Gourdine, thank you for your investment!"

Brother Mark Tillman
34th General President
Alpha Phi Alpha Fraternity, Incorporated

"The Founders of Alpha Phi Alpha Fraternity Inc. achieved extraordinary accomplishments with ordinary means. This book, Jewels, an historical account of their heroic efforts, in the face of insurmountable odds, is one that should not only be required reading for all young men who wish to cross the "burning sands" of our beloved Fraternity, but for anyone desirous of leaving a mark in this word that can never be erased."

Brother Marc H. Morial
President and CEO
National Urban League

"To "know" history one must memorize dates, names and events. However, to "appreciate" history, one must gain insight into the conditions that led to the events, or to paraphrase Indian lore – "walk a mile in their shoes." Jewels provides the insight into the conditions that preceded the founding of one of the great institutions of our day – Alpha Phi Alpha Fraternity, Inc. – by going behind the scenes enabling the reader to stride in the path of those visionary individuals.

Jewels is more than a recordation of history, but a treatise of the mindset of young men not content with the norm, but willing to risk stepping to the forefront. The reader will feel as if they are living with the Jewels as they establish the foundation for this significant fraternal structure continuing its growth to this day. Prepare to learn not only "how", but also "why" the Jewels chose to plant the seed that continues to germinate 100 years later."

Brother LeRoy Lowery, III
Past Eastern Region Vice President
Alpha Phi Alpha Fraternity, Incorporated

"This book effectively puts the founding of one of Black America's most important organizations into time, place and situation. It captures the spirit of the young men who dare to establish the nation's first fraternity for African-American college men."

Brother Stan Verrett
Anchor
ESPN Sportscenter

"Not every novelist can take a true story and put a creative spin on it. But Darrius Jerome Gourdine pulls this off with an exciting and captivating book that takes the reader into the beginnings of America's greatest fraternity, Alpha Phi Alpha Fraternity, Inc. It's a must read for anyone interested I moving beyond the history and into the lives of the seven founders of Alpha."

Brother Lawrence C. Ross Jr.
Author: "The Divine Nine: The History of African
American Fraternities and Sororities"
"The Ways of Black Folks: A Year in the Life of a People"
"Friends With Benefits"

"With such imagination, it is only fitting that the first African American Greek fraternity has achieved the goals it set out from the beginning... Darrius Jerome Gourdine brings to life the fraternal sprit and people who put it all in motion... great job!"

Brother Marc Gay
R&B Singer
Shai

"Citing Booker T. and Brother W.E.B., Jewels serves as a conduit bridging the gap afforded by the struggle of many. This book justifiably re-counts the founding of Alpha Phi Alpha as a symbol for educational advancement and social change. It's a gratifying journey to read how the fact fuses itself into fiction while experiencing this literary work."

Brother Barion L. Grant
Oscar Nominated Associate Producer
Tupac: Resurrection

"Darrius Jerome Gourdine is an absolute connoisseur of African American fraternity and sorority life. I can think of no better person to reconstruct the inner workings of Alpha's founding fathers into a novel that all can enjoy."

Brother C. Brian Williams
Founder & Director
Step Afrika!

"At such a time when contemporary African America life is beleaguered with dysfunction, historical African American novels such as Jewels provide us with a much needed, theoretical road map for the future. Jewels entertains and informs with unequivocal dexterity."

Brother Derek Fordjour
Artist
The 7 Jewels
Filmmaker
Co-creator of The Black Sorority Project

"A smart and engrossing novel. Reveals both the vision and failty of the young med who found the couage to launch Black fraternity lige at a time when such acts of audacity from African Americans regularly provoked lynchings and other forms of racial terror. Brother Darrius, a brother who has embodied the Alpha Phi Alpha spirit since joining the fraternity as a Howard University undergraduate, is the ideal person to render this fascinating story.

Brother Russell Rickford
Author
"Spoken Soul: The Story of Black English"
"Betty Shabazz: A Journey of Strength from Wife to Widow to Heroine"

"Darrius Jerome Gourdine is a powerful "wordsmith" who provides passion and brilliant insight as he tells the story of the seven young mn who created one of our country's most revered and renowned African American organizations."

Brother Eugene Williams, Jr.

Educator, Motivational Speaker, Author
"I Am The Darker Brother"
"Reflections of a Confused Middle Class Black Youth"
"The 'Raisin-In-Milk' Syndrome: Ten Survival Tips for Black Students at Predominantly White Colleges and Universities"

"Goodwill is the Monarch of this House... In an astonishing novel, Darrius Jerome Gourdine captures not only the spirit of the men who founded the fraternity, but he has captured and brought to life the spirit of Alpha Phi Alpha. Through his words, the reader is transformed into a true witness to living history."

Brother Richard A. Chiles
Correspondent
CBS News

"Brother Gourdine's captivating storytelling abilities offers readers an inside perspective of the zeal, intellect, imagination, and courage of seven young African American men who shared a vision of academic excellence and selfless service to the community. Explore the story of the birth of the first African American Greek fraternity as told from the minds of its founders."

Brother Nachee Miller
Lieutenant Colonel, US Army
Professor of Military Science, Howard University

"A round of applause and a standing 06! to Darrius Jerome Gourdine and Jewels: The Story of the Founding of Alpha Phi Alpha. The story is extensively researched and wonderfully written. Gourdine is successful in combining history and literature to create a fascinating reading experience and great work of new historicism. Jewels is a must read for Black Greeks, history buffs and fiction readers alike."

Brother D. Lee Hatchett
Author
The Black Angel Trilogy

"Brother Darrius' book brings life and spirit to our dear fraternity. It represents one moment in time in American history that shows the courage and responsibility of being the first African American fraternity. Jewels captures the hearts, love and passion Alpha is and shares why we as Alpha men must continue to fight to uplift not only Black America, but the world."

Brother Dr. Richard T. James, Jr.
Author
For Your Eyes Only

"Alpha Phi Alpha possesses the distinction of first introducing the conception of a broad social responsibility into the ideals of the American collegiate fraternity. Never has the time been more ripe for us to live up to this heritage."

Jewel Henry Arthur Callis

A

"I'm prepared. I'm prepared." If I keep telling myself that, at some point I actually may convince myself of the same. "I'm very much prepared." I look toward the stage which from my vantage is a long way off. I'm next in line to address my fellow schoolmates. Students are behind me, practicing their own presentations, walking back and forth and shuffling nervously. Mary Heddleworth is on the stage right now singing the Star Spangled Banner. Everyone says she has a good singing voice and will someday be famous. She is the picture of the southern belle in her pig tails, clean new dress, and picture perfect smile. I'm next. "I'm prepared."

"Henry pay attention, you never know, you may preach one day yourself. Or be a scholar or a public speaker." My father says.

"Yes sir."

"When you speak for the audience, always keep your head up. Look at as many Colored folk in the face as you can. Show yourself strong. You understand me?"

"Yes sir."

"For the White folk, glance at their faces. Move your head this way as you talk so you never stay staring at one of 'em for too long." My father lowers his voice even though we are the only ones in the house. "Crackers get nervous when we stare at em!" I laugh.

The applause of the students brings me back into the present as Mary has concluded her tribute to the United States.

"Wasn't that nice? Wonderful job Mary." Our headmaster Mr. Beaverton smiles as Mary as she curtsies and walks off stage in my direction. Mr. Beaverton is a burly White man who says he is interested in educating Negroes with Whites and an equal South for the Colored man. He's even had

Colored people at his home for dinner, or so I heard.

"The next presenter is one of our graduating seniors. He will be presenting a speech for us today. Mr. Henry Callis."

I feel a pat on my back as I move forward to take the stage. I look back and see my classmate Tim, "Good luck Henry."

Everyone claps as I step across the stage. Mr. Beaverton is smiling at me and stepping away from the microphone. My papers are together, my notes are prepared and I have rehearsed the Atlanta Exposition Address a few times over. I'm prepared.

I look across the students and see many Colored faces, many White students too. Stand strong. Glance at the White faces.

"Mr. President and Gentlemen of the board of directors and citizens. One-third of the population of the South is of the Negro race No enterprise seeking the material, civil, or moral welfare of this section can disregard this element of your population and reach the highest success. I but convey to you, Mr. President and Directors, the sentiment of the masses of my face when I say that in no way have the value and manhood of the American Negro been more fittingly and generously recognized than by the managers of this magnificent Exposition at every stage of its progress"

The face of a White student catches my attention in particular as I'm gazing through the audience. "Keep going." Everyone's eyes are fixated on me. There is absolutely no movement at all or sound in the auditorium. There's only my voice and the words of Booker T. Washington."

"A ship lost at sea for many days suddenly sighted a friendly vessel. From the mast of the unfortunate vessel was seen a signal. 'Water, water we die of thirst!' The answer from the friendly vessel at once came back, 'Cast down your bucket where you are.' And a third and fourth signal for water was answered, 'Cast down your bucket where you are.' The captain of the distressed vessel, at last heeding the injunction, cast down his bucket, and it came up full of fresh, sparkling water from the mouth of the Amazon River. To those of my race who depend on bettering their condition in a foreign land or who underestimate the importance of cultivating friendly relations with the Southern white man, who is their next-door neighbor, I would say: 'Cast down your bucket where you are' – cast it down in making friends in every manly way of the people of all races by who we are surrounded."

One Negro student claps loudly but is quickly quieted by his instructor. I continue, glancing down at my notes but quickly raising my head to address my audience... the audience... the schoolmates... the friends... the Atlanta Exposition.

"To those of the white race who look to the incoming of those of foreign birth and strange tongue and habits for the prosperity of the South; were it permitted I would repeat what I say to my own race, 'Cast down your bucket where you are.' Cast it down among the eight millions of Negroes whose habits you know, whose fidelity and love you have tested in days when to have proved treacherous meant the ruin of your firesides. Cast down your bucket amount these people who have, without strikes and labor wars, tilled your fields, cleared your forests, built your railroads and cities, and brought forth treasures from the bowels of the earth, and helped make possible this magnificent representation of the progress of the South."

I did it! I got past my favorite part of the speech! Professor Washington's words are now bouncing off every wall in the auditorium and resounding off every empty seat in the balcony. My favorite aspect of Booker T. Washington's philosophy is his aggressive nature in dealing with race relations. He doesn't back down from his opinion and he isn't afraid to voice it in any arena. The most difficult part of the speech for me is next, the rhyme. If anything, I know I've prepared myself for this. Without looking down..."The lase of changeless justice bind, oppressor with oppressed; and close as sin and suffering joined; we march to fate abreast."

I know dad is proud of how I delivered that part, emulating him as much as I could. Mother is looking down on me too... proud of her Henry.

"I pledge that in your effort to work out the great and intricate problem which God has laid at the doors of the South, you shall have at all times the patient, sympathetic help of my race; only let this be constantly in mind, that, while from representation in these buildings of the product of field, of forest, of mine, of beyond material benefits will be that higher good, that, let us pray God, will come, in a blotting out of sectional differences and racial animosities and suspicions, in a determination to administer absolute justice, in a willing obedience among all classes to the mandates of law. This, then, coupled without material prosperity, will bring into our beloved South a new heaven and a new earth. Thank you."

I must be in a daze. Did I finish the entire speech... already... well yes I did. It's obvious. Everyone is standing up clapping. It catches me by surprise as there was a clear split second from the time I finished speaking to the time when everyone stands. I don't remember seeing people leaving their seats. At this time, everyone is standing... even my father. He however is the only person not clapping. Instead, he has his arms boldly folded across his chest. This is his stance when he finished a particularly perfect sermon. A look of satisfaction! He is smiling proudly. That warms my heart as I turn in the opposite direction of the headmaster.

"Mr. Henry, wait, wait just a minute."

Mr. Beaverton has called me back toward the microphone. I hope for nothing embarrassing. He holds both hands up to quiet the crowed from their applause. "Ladies and gentlemen, I just would like to acknowledge Henry on a wonderful speech. I personally have heard this speech by Mr. Booker T. Washington delivered before, but never with such magnitude and driving force. It was as if Mr. Booker was here himself, delivering the speech for us!"

I had a feeling he was going to embarrass me. Everyone begins to applaud me and I smile out of generous good nature.

"I think we might want to call Mr. Henry here, the second Booker T. Washington!"

"Oh no sir, I could never live up to such a name. Henry Callis is enough for me."

"Oh don't be so modest Henry." Mr. Beaverton has turned toward me and forsaken the audience. "We're very proud of you here Henry and we trust that you will go far in life." He turns back to address my family and schoolmates. "Henry will proudly represent us in the fall at Cornell University! Congratulations Henry and good luck."

"Thank you sir!" I walks offstage half embarrassed and half proud of my performance, and half relieved it's over. Too many halves but I am certain of one fact, I am by no means a young Booker T. Booker T. Washington is a scholar amongst scholars. I would only hope that one day I can ascertain half of what he has accomplished through his research. Now that would be an accomplishment.

"Great job Booker!" Tim congratulates or insults, the line between the two is thin as his pat on my shoulder suggests congratulatory yet his tone and laughter insist insult. I smile back at him and try to do him one better.

"Let's see how you do, and see what name you receive!" My statement doesn't quite have the same dichotomy as his, but we both laugh nonetheless.

The remainder of my matriculation time at Central quickly escapes me as did the rendering of the Atlanta Exposition. With my thoughts clearly focused on Cornell, I seemed overly anxious to be done with the pomp and circumstance of one level of education and eager to begin the pursuit of the next.

With that, I stand on the campus of Cornell "prepared" and ready to begin my new life. I remember Cornell from a visit when I was much younger. Roy and I were here and although it was many years ago, I remember it as vivid as if it were this very summer. What most impressed me then and now was the graduate students. One in particular, Mr. Edward Brooks, took it upon himself to share with me some insight into his future in a law practice and his matriculation time at Cornell. How fascinating that as he ponders a new level and transition in leaving this life, I so eagerly anticipate all that this same life brings here for me on campus.

"Mr. Henry!"

I turn immediately to see Nathaniel, my new comrade approaching. The adjustment of not being known by many in school is still quite new to me as only a handful or so students here know me by name. I've made it a point to try and meet and remember the other Black students here. "Nathaniel, how are you?"

"I'm fine sir, and you?" he replies.

"On my way to Sociology class. You going to class as well?

"No, I have a meeting with a number of students in my concentration."

"What are you studying?"

"Agriculture."

"You did mention that to me before."

"Yes." He smiles. "If I want to continue my studies, I'd better hurry. I'd hate to be late." Nathaniel laughs and pushes his thin rimmed glasses up his nose. It seems as if he'll drop every book he's holding as he is weighted down with both books and papers. He maintains well as he bids me farewell for now.

"Right. I'll speak with you again." I say.

"Sure Henry. I'll see you later."

As Nathaniel walks on to his meeting, I recognize my own tardiness and gain a sense of urgency in getting to my class. Sociology is one of the subjects I enjoy as the subject matter is interesting and the professor even more intriguing. Professor Wilcox has an extraordinaire mind and a fascinating theory on social issues. His views contrast greatly with those of Professor Washington, who's ideologies I'd become acquainted with while at Central, Professor Wilcox leans more toward the side of W.E.B. DuBois, who's Niagara Movement of the summer raised many an eyebrow in Negro circles. As controversial as the conference may have been, I have to acknowledge the courageous effort it took to orchestrate great thinkers among our race and rally them to a call of action.

"Henry!"

I turn to see Victor, a friend who also graduated from Central and now attends Cornell. He is walking with another male student. "Late for class as well I see," I say.

Victor smiles as they hastily approach. "The walk from building to building is unfamiliar. I'm used to only traveling from room to room." We laugh together as he pats me on the shoulder. "This Is Christopher. You may have seen him in our class as well. "Christopher, this is Henry Callis from my hometown of Binghamton." Christopher glances my way but scarcely acknowledges me, very much to the embarrassment of Victor. I know his glance all too well. Growing up in New York didn't afford me the blunt racism of the South, rather the overt racism of the North. White people that would have little to do with Negroes would prefer the members of the race disappear one day as if in a cloud of smoke.

"I suppose we can all walk into class together and be tardy on one accord." I rescue Victor from this uncomfortable silence.

He smiles. "Yes, I suppose."

The house itself is tremendous. If nothing else, the edifice is a remarkable piece of architecture. The stonewall construction is characteristically that of Ithaca and a boastful landmark of the Cornell campus. Most of the buildings on campus share the rocky cobblestone structure, tall windows, and great landscape. However, few have the same mysterious appeal as that of the Theta Beta Pi Fraternity house. I feel in a great sense more privileged than the average Negro student in that I have the opportunity to witness firsthand the inner activities of a fraternity. At the same notion, I realize I am on the outside of their world gazing in with as much awe as everyone else.

"Good afternoon George."

"Good afternoon sir." I reply. "Off to ride?"

"Yes. I gather that is fairly obvious."

I smile. John's attire clearly indicates that he is indeed taking a ride on his bike. Dark knickers, vest with riding jacket, matching apple jack cap and riding shoes.

"I thought I would ride across campus to the field. It's a nice day for a ride. Some of the fraternity members are playing football today. Thought I'd watch."

"Not going to participate in the games yourself?" I ask.

"Oh no. Not much of an athlete myself. I'll be the fraternity bystander in those regards."

John, or JR as he is referred to often, is in his third year as a student at Cornell. Both he and his father are members of Theta Beta Pi Fraternity and John resides in the fraternity house. He is one of the first members of the fraternity that I met when I began working here at the house.

It always works well for me to work weekends at the house because most of the time the fraternity members were off doing various activities. It provides me with an opportunity to investigate their structure or read my studies in a quiet environment.

There are several photographs in the house. Alumnus members of the fraternity are pictured along with fraternity classes of prior years. The coat of arms hangs over the entry to the reading room and the fraternity letters are in every corridor. Residence rooms are upstairs and a mini dining facility with a bar is in the basement. Secret meetings are held in what is referred to as the board room and initiations are held upstairs in the top of the house. I don't know a lot about what takes place in the initiation ceremonies except they have many lit candles and hooks over the heads of the initiates.

It's an intriguing culture, fraternity life. One that's mystery entices many of the campus society while equally frightening away many more. With such names as Alpha Delta Phi, Phi Kappa Psi, Sigma Alpha Epsilon, Phi Delta Theta and more, these fraternities compete for the most grandiose house, the most authentic antique furniture, and the cleverest way to go about their external campus life.

It was an ironic meeting between me and Henry Callis, a freshman who works at the Sigma Alpha Epsilon Fraternity house. As odd as it may seem, working in the house creates a somewhat small allegiance to this organization, more than the others. Upon meeting Henry, who feels the same toward his friends at Sigma Alpha Epsilon, I remember us laughing as we wagered which fraternity would win the campus welcome games. Both of our groups however came short to Sigma Phi Fraternity.

I barely heard the knock on the front door. John, Michael

and I are all in the house. I know Michael is asleep and since John is engrossed in his studies, I choose to answer. There is a couple at the door, a young debonair gentleman and quite an attractive lady on his arm. He removes his derby and quickly situates it underneath his arm as I answer the door.

"May I help you sir?"

"Good afternoon, my name is Lincoln Wadsworth and this is my fiancée Eunice Smithe."

She smiles at me and offers her hand.

I take her hand and receive her salutation. "Hello, my name is George Kelley. Please come in."

"Thank you Messr. Kelley. I'm an alumnus of both the university and Theta Beta Pi." Lincoln says. "I wish to show my finance the house that I once called home." he says as he looks around as if he has never been inside the fraternity house before.

"Are any of the brothers in the house at the moment?"

"Yes, two right now. Michael Davenport and John Reynolds." I reply.

"Oh yes, I remember them both. It will be good to say hello to them." He turns to his fiancée. "Honey, let me show you my fraternity class here on the wall."

"What class were you a member of?" I ask standing behind them both.

"1903. I recently graduated and now work in New York City." He doesn't take his glance from the mounted framed picture on the wall. "Is this your first year at Cornell George?"

"Yes. I formerly was at RPI. I'm continuing my studies here now at the University."

Lincoln turns around to acknowledge my statement. "Oh really? How interesting."

"Who's that in the parlor George?" John says descending from the stairwell.

"Mr. Lincoln Wadsworth and his fiancée," I turn to her, "please forgive me, but your name once again."

"Eunice. Eunice Smithe," she says quietly, acknowledging me with a pretty smile but speaking more so to John.

"JR, it's good to see you brother."

Lincoln and JR embrace and he more formally is introduced to Miss Smithe. Their conversation now becomes more incoherent to me as I drift into the background of their fraternal matters.

"Henry, it's obvious. It had to have been a bad idea. Why else would they have held it above the border?"

Victor knows me a lot better than this. He's seen me debate a good point. He's actually seen me debate a terrible position and win. My determination now is whether he argues with me to hear my skills at debate or whether he actually believes his stance.

"Why not conduct the conference in New York?" Victor asks already knowing the answer to his question. "Buffalo would have been prime. Binghamton even. What is the racial disparity in Binghamton? Your greatest thinkers may have been welcomed."

"To argue the case of racial disparity in the north, even New York is absurd at best. To even suggest Binghamton, Rochester, or Buffalo is as senseless as offering Birmingham or Montgomery, Alabama. The fact that you personally haven't seen a lynching doesn't mean lifeless bodies don't swing from branches. I don't have to inform you that no hotel would provide a meeting place for twenty nine Negroes with the agenda of the uplift of the race and full citizenship for the Negro." I don't care to test his skill for the sport of argument. I stand on my point.

"The Niagara Conference in and of itself is timely, necessary and dare I say overdone?"

Victor smiles an insulting smile. I know he means nothing by it toward the conference called by Dr. Dubois on behalf of every American Negro. He'd rather insult my expertise at debate compared to his less than valiant effort. His point is not as strong however, making it all the easier. The fact is that the Niagara Conference is the talk of the far and few between Negro students on campus. We recognize that this is indeed a strong statement and a pivotal turn in our history. If nothing else, it has energized us to mobilize ourselves to a greater sense of unity.

"You've always been a great debater Henry," Victor concedes.

"You're not bad. Why didn't you ever grace us with your presence in Congress?"

Victor laughs, the laugh that I'm more used to from my high school comrade. "Debate is your forte Henry, not flattery." We share a pretty good laugh from that one.

It's a beautiful day. Between classes I happened to see Victor walking and we decided to spend a few moments on a bench talking about our campus experience so far. How we began discussing the conference is unknown. It originated somewhere, grew from nowhere and ended abruptly. I wonder how dad would've responded to my oratorical technique today... staring directly into Victor's face, cracker or not. Look him down, speak him down.

There are so many students going to and fro in front and behind us. It's remarkable to fathom only half a dozen Negro students to the ratio of so many White students. Such is the way of the world. All the more reason the call to unite and get to know one another informally.

I see an intriguing sight that causes me to stop laughing and look twice. "Excuse me Victor. Pardon me but I need to speak to someone that I recognize."

"I need to be off and on my way as well. Until we speak again," says Victor with the familiar pat on my shoulder.

I smile back at him but quickly redirect my attention toward the student walking on campus that caught my eye. Although I did mention to Victor that I recognized this fellow, I actually have no clue on earth who this gentleman is. He is rather odd looking in his get up and if it were not for the fact that he is of the persuasion, I probably would poke fun at him as others are probably doing right now. He's walking rather swiftly albeit he is a heavy fellow. A very confident stride as he seems to know exactly where he is going and is moving with quite a purpose. I clumsily make it apparent that I am attempting to catch up with him and get his attention. I catch up to him from behind.

"Excuse me... uh, excuse me." I say.

The fellow turns around to reveal a tight fitted cadet's uniform, at least a size too small. He's wearing round glasses that compliment his even rounder face. He's also carrying a saxophone underneath his arm.

"Good afternoon sir, my name is Henry Callis."

He shifts the saxophone to shake my extended hand. "Vertner W. Tandy. Pleased to meet you." he says.

"Vertner Tandy. I can't say I've seen you on campus before," I say with a smile.

"Same goes for me Mr. Henry. It's good to make your acquaintance nonetheless. First year student?"

"Yes, and yourself?"

"First year at Cornell. I'm transplanted here," he laughs at his own statement before he continues, "I once was a Tuskegeegian and now I'm a Cornellian." He laughs hard at that one, tightening his grip on his saxophone as to not drop it.

"Really?" My curiosity is peaked now, much more that my amusement. "Are you familiar with Professor Washington?"

"Am I familiar with Profe... am I familiar with Professor Washington?" He laughs and then clears his throat. "I'm not only familiar with Dr. Booker T., but I'm one of his prized pupils!" Vertner's chest pokes out, as mine would, had I been a student of Professor Washington.

I'm very hesitant to believe him as he seems like the jovial type. He really could be pulling my leg. If for nothing else, why leave Tuskegee Institute if Booker T. Washington is a personal mentor? It's far-fetched and somewhat unbelievable to say the least. "You're one of his prized pupils?" I surprisingly ask.

"I most certainly am... or was I should say."

"Imagine the irony then, you and I meeting like this. In high school they referred to me as the second Booker T. Washington."

Vertner takes a step back and clearly is holding in a laugh. He looks me up and down thoroughly, then lets out a laugh so loud that other passerby students stop and notice. "The second Booker T. Washington? You? Seriously?"

"I didn't take to the name too kindly myself. I felt unworthy of the honor. Highly unlikely." I admit to Vertner, not knowing if his laughter was at my expense or not.

"You must be an intellectual then."

"I dare not think so." I respond. "It's just what others have commented about me. I delivered the Atlanta Exposition address and was pinned the name afterward."

"I guess there are worst names to be named, or worst people to be named after. Take it as a compliment Henry."

I smile.

"Or is it Booker? Shall I call you Henry Washington or would you prefer Booker Callis?" He laughs loudly again and I have to laugh along with him.

"You're quite a character!" I say laughingly.

"Thank you... I suppose. Unless this is a jab you're taking at me and now you've pinned me with a name!" He smiles as he makes his statement notifying me of his jest and causing me to smile with him.

"Right this way sirs. You two should like our accommodations. We're simple people."

I smile harder then I'd been smiling already. "It's so awkward to hear you refer to us as sirs. You certainly don't have to address me with that title." I say.

"Me neither ma'am," says Morgan smiling as well.

"My husband and I are polite folk. If you're ever in need of anything sirs, you just let us know."

"Thank you kindly. You did mention that already," I reply.

"Now tell me your names one more time. I want to be

accurate with my introductions." she says.

"Sure ma'am. Robert Harold Ogle."

"Robert Harold Ogle. Nice name."

I laugh. "Thank you Mrs. Singleton."

"And you?" she asks.

"Morgan Phillips."

"Morgan Phillips. Where did you mention that you two were from?"

"We didn't mention but Washington, DC." Morgan says.

"Oh Washington. I've never been to our nation's capital. The home of President Theodore Roosevelt!"

We both enjoy ourselves laughing at that one.

"Mr. Bullfeathers himself!" Mrs. Singleton says. I'm immediately surprised at her statement even as she laughs.

"What was that Mrs. Singleton?"

"The president doesn't use expletives in speech. A fine gentleman he is. When the president becomes agitated, he yells bullfeathers instead of... you know, instead of something else."

"Is that so?" Morgan asks.

"That's what my husband told me at least." She laughs again.

Mrs. Singleton shows Morgan to his room first. As she unlocks the door, my curiosity is at the same height as his as I am anxious to see both his and my living quarters. "Here you are Morgan. This is your room"

Morgan walks into the room and places his suitcase down. He smiles politely at his humble new residence. "Thank you Mrs. Singleton and I must also thank Mr. Singleton." The room is equipped with the basic necessities; a bed, a dresser with mirror, a desk, a chair, and an armoire. "I should do fine here."

"Yes you will," she says to Morgan with a smile. "Now off to your room Robert."

"Thank you ma'am," I reply. She shows me my room,

directly across the hall from Morgan's with an identical set up. As Morgan did, I place my suitcase on the floor of my new room and take it all in. My new home, here at Cornell U.

"I'll let you gentlemen get settled and let my husband know that you found the rooms to your approval."

"Thank you Mrs. Singleton," I say, Morgan repeating.

The house is perfect for my purposes here at the university. Quiet study. Located at the bottom of East State Street, the home of the Singletons is a short distance from the campus. Morgan's and my rooms are upstairs in the house, Archie and Annie's bedroom downstairs on the level below, and Annie's Ladies' Exchange is street level. The Ladies' Exchange is a modest storefront run by Mrs. Annie with very punctual hours and a very unique list of trinkets, ornaments, and antiques.

"Robert!"

I step into the doorway of my room to respond to Morgan who is standing in the doorway of his.

"What do you really think of our new home?" He asks at a whisper as not to alert the Singletons of my answer good or bad. I lean against the doorway and cross my arms. "It's a far cry from home and Cornell is a lot different than the M School. The Singletons are gracious hosts and nice people. I think I'm going to like it here. What about you?"

"I echo your sentiments exactly. I know we're going to extract all that we can from this experience my friend."

"What were your findings Benjamin?"

Benjamin, my classmate responds, "In the activity of photosynthesis, light is captured by chlorophyll. It is the substance responsible for the color in plant life."

"That's correct. Please add your findings," Professor Hunt addresses the entire class, "the role of membranous sacs in the photosynthetic process. For your next class session we will discuss and review. Come prepared from your own diligent study, well versed on the subject matter. This concludes today's lecture. Thank you."

I quickly gather my belongings and rush toward the front of the room. Not to speak with Professor Hunt but to his assistant, Mr. Poindexter. We were acquainted a few sessions ago and I received word that he wishes to speak with me. Mr. Poindexter, or C.C. as he prefers, is a graduate student here in the Department of Agronomy and well versed in the matters of agriculture.

"Mr. Poindexter, if you have a moment." He turns around from placing papers in a knapsack for the professor.

"Nathaniel. Yes, I do wish to speak to you. If you can give me a slight moment to collect myself and the doctor's things." C.C. says.

"Sure. I have time." I reply.

C.C. is a strong spoken man who is extremely sure of himself. His confidence lends to his character and he carries himself well. His face is oddly familiar in that he gives the impression that you already know him, even though you may not have been introduced. His nose is broad and his eyebrows cast a shadow on his eyes as they protrude forward. He demands attention, whether he is speaking or not, simply by his overwhelming presence. He's not overbearing. Instead an individual who's presence is felt in a crowded room. C.C.'s concentration is agronomy and he's in the graduate student's program.

C.C. accepts final instructions from Professor Hunt and turns toward me. He smiles a welcoming smile as he approaches.

"If you have a moment Nathaniel, I'd like to walk and talk with you." C.C. has the type of personality where you want to accompany him.

"Sure. I accept your invitation. I have some time before my next appointment in class." I say.

"Good."

I follow him out of the auditorium as the aisle is too narrow for us to walk side by side. He begins speaking nonetheless as I listen attentively.

"There was a student in the agriculture department last fall, 1904. He was establishing himself in his studies and more than likely going to be a junior intern for Dr. Hunt. Unfortunately he has not returned this semester. He more than likely has met financial challenges that are preventing him from continuing his education, continuing his education here at Cornell at least."

"That is unfortunate."

"Yes it is. Every Negro should have the opportunity to continue his studies. Especially if they persevere to the university level." C.C. continues, "I think that those of us already here have the best opportunity to assist those who may be having troubles somehow."

"What was this student's name?" I ask.

"Francis. Understand Nathaniel, it isn't Francis that I'm referring to alone. Every Negro who began their studies and somehow aren't able to complete them. There are more than just him."

"Is it that much of a problem here?"

He replies, "I don't have to educate you on the mentality of a northern White university in the educating of Negroes. They'd probably rather not. They'll never admit that of course."

"Of course not."

We step outside into the autumn air. I tighten my scarf around my neck as the wind brings the familiar New York sting. It's not as cold as a harsh winter but it definitely has made the transition from summer. The subtle sting is in the air. C.C. tightens his blazer around him but doesn't adorn an overcoat, hat, or scarf. He braves the elements and continues speaking without so much as a break in his dissertation.

"Somehow it's our responsibility to those coming behind us to assure their wellbeing and support their continuance here." C.C. says.

"How do we go about that?" I ask. "Are we not all in the same predicament as they? Removing yourself of course, having completed the undergrad portion of your studies. How are we to help?"

"I have an idea. A philosophy actually, that we are stronger united then separated. The Negroes at Cornell are few and far between. We rarely communicate with one another and may, each of us, posses some characteristic or gifting that could encourage others to strive and persevere. This assessment stands for myself as well as I am even in a greater position to help. As you said, I'm a graduate student. I definitely have a greater access to resources."

"Afternoon Mr. Poindexter." A few students walking past salute C.C. He waves and smiles but continues to address me as if he hadn't spoken to them all."

"I have, for example, OTQ's in my office that I know would be helpful. I could probably collect more from some of my comrades."

"OTQ's? I'm sorry but I'm not familiar."

I'm sorry," C.C. says, "old test questions. Most professors recycle the same exams over and over."

"They don't alter their questions at all?"

"Yes they do but to know how the professors are asking the questions will still help. If you have reserved all of your notes for Negro students that may take the same classes next year that you complete this year, you would be able to help those coming behind you." he offers.

"That's true. I could do that."

"Now, imagine if the few Negroes on campus could ban together for the common good and do the same for each of us, or each of you. We could at least present a solution for those having problems with their studies. The financial aspect would be a much larger task to bear, but not to do something to assist at all would prove monumental over time."

"These are all wonderful ideas C.C. but what are you driving at? I'm not sure I understand what you're attempting to suggest." I say.

"I'm driving at change Nathaniel. I'm driving at making a difference. How much of a difference we could make!" C.C.'s tone carries so much passion. "The reason I needed to speak to you privately is to ask you how many colored students you know personally."

"Well there's Morgan and Robert from the M School in Washington." I reply.

"Yes. Who else?"

"Of course there's Charles from the agriculture department."

"Charles Chapman?" he asks.

"Yes, Charles Chapman. Then I know Henry Callis. I met him during opening week." I say.

"My idea is to galvanize these students." C.C. says. "The students that you know, the students that they know, the ones that I know." We stop walking in front of the campus administration building. "Mobilize the Negro students on campus, subtly of course. I would like to invite each of these students to my residence to talk about some of the very ideas I've shared with you today Nathaniel. We need to create dialogue drawing from these philosophies. We need to at least make an attempt at unity, if nothing else, for the sake of one another."

"The idea is intriguing. One that I believe would work well and do exactly as you noted, unify Negroes on campus to one common goal. Sustaining and encouraging each other." I find it quite ironic to discuss such an idea standing directly in front of the Cornell Administration building. What would some of the university elite think of such a notion as Negroes mobilizing under their noses?

C.C. shows the first sign of the wind cutting through his blazer as he pats his arms for warmth. He looks around in the air as if to see the source of the crisp wind. His resolve however is unmoved.

"I want to hold an informal get together at my home. I've already spoken with the owner of the house, Mr. Newton, and he's taken strongly to the idea. It appears he became more excited than I did and I brought the suggestion." C.C. laughs. I smile. "Do you think you will have the opportunity to see some of the other students that you mentioned in order to inform them of the get together?"

"Certainly. I can visit Morgan and Robert and inform them."

"Fine. The others?"

"I can attempt to find them and let them know as well. Where is your home?"

"Are you familiar with North Albany Street?"

"North Albany Street. I'm not familiar." I reply.

"Are you familiar with Campus Road?"

"Yes, I do know where that is."

"Good." C.C. smiles. "I wasn't too sure, remembering that you are new here. The home is walking distance from campus. Very accessible. You can walk from Campus Road and be there in minutes."

"That's fine. What are the directions? Should I write it down?"

"I don't feel the need. You're educated. You can remember." Both C.C. and I laugh as another student acknowledges him.

"Mr. Poindexter, good to see you sir."

"Hello Clarence! Good to see you too!" He turns his attention back to me. "If you take Campus Road and make a left onto Steward Avenue..."

I repeat his directions. "Left onto Stewart Avenue..."

"Then take a right turn onto East Buffalo Avenue. Finally turning right onto North Albany Street Mr. Newton's house is 421."

"Okay. I can certainly bring that back to my own remembrance. I can spread the word to my fellow classmates as well."

"Great!" C.C. announces with a proclamation that causes even I to be proud that his exclamation is toward something I said. "I'm going to notify Mr. Newton and begin to prepare. There's much to do in hosting fellows at your home."

"I'm sure. It's a great idea C.C." I say.

"Sure. Thank you. I'll be off now but when I see you again, I will notify you of Mr. Newton's response and the date and time of the gathering."

"Splendid."

"Take care," as he is walking away and closing his blazer around his tall frame, "and I will speak with you shortly Nathaniel!"

"Good bye." I call out.

Without another word CC. is off to his next destination

and I to mine. The thought of what he offered doesn't escape my conscious mind easily. A means to help students coming behind those already enrolled and matriculating at Cornell. What a great asset that could be to aspiring Negroes. Reserving exams for future classes. I don't know if I would've come up with such an idea myself. C.C. certainly has the advantage of being a graduate student and having experienced these things already. How much better he may have done with the same guidance he is suggesting.

As I continue to walk and remember the task that C.C. placed on my shoulders, I see my friend Henry walking toward me in the distance. Henry has a pleasant smile and a very warm and inviting face. I shake his hand as he approaches and I bid him hello. "Good afternoon Henry."

"How are you Nathaniel?" he asks, never losing his smile.

"I'm fine and yourself?"

"Getting ready for a bitter winter. Even for those of us from upstate."

I laugh. "Perhaps what I will share with you will warm at least your spirit. A graduate student in my department has invited me to an informal gathering at his residence on North Albany. He is interested in calling the Negro students together under the banner of unity and togetherness. In order to help one another and those coming behind us."

"Really? Who is this graduate student?" Henry asks.

"His name is Mr. C.C. Poindexter and he lives at 421 North Albany Street. He has explained to me all that he would like to accomplish through the gathering and has championed the cause of rallying us together. I must say that I am rather impressed with his presentation and look forward to the meeting."

"How far have the invitations been extended? What is the criteria to join the gathering?"

"He presented me with the task of notifying any Negro students that I know and to place the same task to you comrades of mine who may know others as well. You've met a few haven't you?" I ask.

Henry takes a moment to think before he responds. "Yes actually, I have met a few. I think this is a grand and necessary idea. I will notify those that I know right away."

"As will I. With our efforts we should be able to gather the lot of us." I say with confidence, knowing everyone will take to this idea heartily as Henry has.

"You know Nathaniel, it's extremely interesting that this Mr. Poindexter has raised this question at this time. I don't know if you're at all familiar with George but he is a friend who works at one of the fraternity houses as I do. We've discussed many nights the idea of a similar group, but for us Negroes." Henry's countenance changes immediately as suddenly as he makes this statement.

"A fraternity for Negroes?"

"We've discussed the idea. I've had conversations with my friends from SAE and he at Theta Beta Pi. Very interesting conversations that I have to admit have peaked both mine and George's curiosities a great deal." Henry is much more serious as he builds upon the idea that C.C. spoke to me about. This is an entirely different element, an interesting one nonetheless. If administration officials would be taken aback by conversations about a gathering to discuss the offering of assistance to our fellow Negroes, they would be overwhelmed by the concept of a Negro fraternity.

"It's a grand idea but how well do you feel it will be received?" I ask with more curiosity now then I expressed with C.C. just a few moments ago.

"I would hope with as much interest as you're expressing right now." Henry smiles again and breaks his countenance.

"Most certainly, I assure you, I will find you and notify you of the date and time of the get together."

"Sir John Reynolds, I dub thee most loyal brother of the order most high!" I proclaim.

JR Laughs a hardy laugh, leaning back and slapping his leg down. "George you're a card with that one! No it isn't like that at all," he says.

"You must tell me then. I earnestly inquire." I imitate a servant asking a question of the king.

"Fine, fine. I did promise to tell you as much as I could." He pauses and collects himself from his laughter. "For me, the club itself is a family heirloom. Both my father and grandfather were members in college."

"Oh?" I reply. "I didn't know that your grandfather was a Theta Beta man as well!"

"Oh yes. He's undoubtedly the reason my father persisted. He and my father have a difference of opinion on most things but that common denominator joins both of them and me."

"Interesting."

"Yes. So my grandfather is much more inclined to talk about his membership when he attended school. For me, it's the friendships that I've established here. It's the brotherhood that we have devoted our college career to build and maintain. It's the camaraderie and the sense of unity."

I attentively listen and am intrigued.

"I wanted Theta Beta to be my choice, not my father's choice for me. Upon meeting the members when I first entered Cornell, I was thoroughly impressed. It was just as my grandfather had described to my father and my father had described to me. I will likely maintain these friendships throughout my professional career, well past the days of Cornell."

"What, if I may ask, is the selection criteria?" I ask.

"Well... " JR pauses and looks at me with a bit of concern. I'm not entirely certain if the question that I raised is only to be known by the members of Theta Beta Pi in which I have trampled on sacred territory. " ...let me ask you first George if I may."

"Certainly," I respond.

"Your reason for asking, and for this conversation in general... and conversations we've had in the past... are you asking about membership for your own accord?" He asks apparently concerned.

"Oh no I'm not. I apologize for not stating my mission initially." His question offers me a bit of relief, in that my curiosity is certainly not driven by my own interest in membership in Theta Beta Pi. I'm more interested in the structure, foundation and institution of fraternity. Carefully choosing my words at this awkward juncture of JR's and my friendship. "I've become curious as to the structure of fraternity. Not in membership in any one in particular but as you know there isn't such an organization for that of the Negro."

JR almost smiles. Not to mimic but pondering the thought. Of course the fraternity system at Cornell is exclusive to Whites. I'm assured this is the same at all universities. To be the first fraternity to integrate, I doubt Theta Beta Pi would choose to be the fraternity best known for that accomplishment. Although the members of Theta Beta Pi in the house as well as those on campus have always treated me with the utmost respect and true spirit of friendship.

"You have to excuse me for my question George. You know I think very highly of you. I always have."

"I know JR. I didn't mean to give you the incorrect impression." I excuse JR and try to create an easier environment toward conversation as ours' was interrupted. "Don't worry any longer about it."

"Sorry George. Anything else you would like to know?" he asks offering to continue.

"Actually yes. The criteria question, you never responded."

"Oh yes!" JR laughs. "The criteria. One must be of high moral standard... until they become members!" He laughs and leans in my direction as if to elbow my arm. He gestures and I laugh. My laugh acknowledges that I understand and do recount instances where members weren't always as friendly toward one another in heated debate. "We require an average scholastic aptitude and a well social character. Theta Beta men have always been athletic. That's where I fall short of the glory of TBPi, I have to admit!" He's right.

"What about legalities of the matter? Documentation? Guidelines?" I ask.

"We have to have a constitution in place that governs our affairs as well as our existence. It was drafted by our members in the same manner as the Constitution of the

40

United States was drafted by our forefathers. It is kept on record and contains all rules, mandates, and regulations that all members adhere to."

"What of the mystery of fraternity life?"

"I, for one, believe it adds to the competition amongst fraternity elite. If they are inquiring about us and us about them, it adds to the general mystique. Most students also approach members with a strong sense of intimidation and humility. Based on our actions and concealing our internal affairs and structure." JR answers matter-of-factly.

"Very interesting." I say. My statement leads to a moment of silence. An almost awkward silence until JR asks a question of his own.

"You mentioned the lack of similar organizations for members of your race. Is this a cause of concern amongst you? Somewhat of a rallying effort for Negroes?"

"I don't believe interest has arisen. Not that it shouldn't. Not that it won't.

"She's so good a house mother that it seems as if my own father hired her to keep watch after me!" Nathaniel, who is always one for a good joke, chuckles at that one.

"She apparently keeps a well prepared house." He says as he looks around my room. "Or should I give you the credit for how tidy your room is?"

"Place that square on my shoulders." I say. "Clean habits are a way of life in the Ogle household."

"From what I can remember then it's a hereditary trait that bypassed the Ogle men!"

We both laugh.

"How have things been faring for you so far? All is well?" I ask changing the subject.

"Yes, things are going as best as can be expected I

supposed. I'm making a firm adjustment. I can admit that it is very different from M." Nathaniel says.

"That is certain. We... " I remember that at times Mr. Singleton walks the halls and can hear our voices clearly, especially now with my bedroom door open. I lower my voice so my statement takes no offense. " ...we are definitely outnumbered by the Whites here. I barely see our Colored students in my day-to-day travels. The few I see I don't see too often. Has that been your experience?"

"Quite the same." He replies. "That is the exact reason I came to visit both you and Morgan. Where is he by the way?"

"I'm not sure. He's usually here by now although he has mentioned looking into possible jobs after classes."

"Very well. I'm sure you can notify him of what I am about to share with you."

"What is it?" I ask.

"There is a graduate student over my department whose name is Charles, referred to as C.C. He spoke with me and informed me that he's hosting a casual get together at his home inviting all Negro students as a means to get to know each other."

"Really?" I'm intrigued at this notion.

"Yes. He's serious about the lack of togetherness on campus amongst Negroes and the fact that we are so few in number and so far between."

I stand up and pass Nathaniel who is leaning against my desk. I close my bedroom door. This conversation is turning from a chat between two familiar buddies to a planning session of the utmost secrecy. Not as it should be seen in any devious light but the nature in itself can be taken several ways. Either way taken, I am further intrigued and curious as to what else he has to share about this graduate student. "What else did C.C. say to you?"

"He told me that there were many more Negro students here only last year. Many have not returned for various reasons he told me." Nathaniel says with a serious tone.

"I had heard that very thing." I reply. "I'd actually heard that from Mrs. Singleton downstairs."

"Your new house mother?" Nathaniel breaks the tone with a quip and I smile.

"Yes." I answer back. "Many cannot afford to remain another year and have to work just to attempt a return. There is no support system for Negroes. None at all."

"C.C. spoke with me about rallying together, forming a group that can help one another with examinations. Even doing our diligence to ensure that we all return each semester, or have summer jobs for extra earnings."

"All of these ideas sound fantastic, but how? How can this all be accomplished?"

Nathaniel pushes his glasses up his nose and folds his arms across his chest. "That has yet to be determined but I'm sure C.C. has ideas as he has been seeing these trends for years now."

"This is all extremely interesting Nate and I can't say that..." there is a heavy knock on my door. I walk past Nate to open it. "Morgan? I didn't hear you come in." Normally one can be heard either on the stairwell or the hall of the house. Since Nathaniel and I were talking, I didn't hear Morgan coming up the stairs.

"Robert I need to talk to you. Nathaniel." Morgan acknowledges Nathaniel without looking at him.

"Morgan." Nathaniel responds.

"What has kept you? Were you inquiring about work like you'd mentioned?" I'm wondering though why Morgan seems frustrated and on edge.

"No not at all. Instead I dealt with a disturbing matter. A very disturbing matter. Look at this." Morgan shows us a few sheets of paper.

"What is this?" Nathaniel asks.

"It is an essay examination from my Philosophy class. Dr. Platt is the instructor's name." Morgan says disgustedly.

The papers have red marks throughout each paragraph and as I page through the document and pass it along to Nathaniel, I begin to see where Morgan's frustration lies. "What happened?" I ask.

Morgan replies immediately. "You can look and see what happened! He tore the document to shreds with his pen indicating that I know nothing of the subject matter. That's as preposterous of a notion as any!"

I've known Morgan Phillips for quite some time and I know him to be a good natured and evenly tempered person. I've never seen him quite this upset, or really upset at all for that matter. He is boiling over and neither I nor Nathaniel know how to respond.

"Morgan," Nathaniel says cautiously, "have you spoken with this Dr... what did you say his name is"?

"Platt. Dr. Maxwell Platt. Yes, I took the time to schedule an appointment to speak with him directly."

"When was this appointment?" I ask.

"This afternoon. That is where I am retuning from. Both he and his student administrator disregarded everything I said about his markings and were rude toward me to say the least. The two of them did all but lynch me on the spot with their words!"

The connotation of lynching is such a vivid and harsh reality that the simple mention of it brings the room to utter silence and serious regard for Morgan's feelings. I really wish words of comfort could come to mind. Nothing does. I mask my inability to think of the best thing to say for the situation by paging through his examination once again.

Morgan breaks his own silence. "If I were a White student, I know they wouldn't have spoken to me the way that they did."

"You're absolutely correct." Nathaniel chimes in. "Absolutely correct about that."

"Nathaniel, why don't you tell Morgan about the meeting?"

"Oh yes! Just that quickly I completely had forgotten! I was so intertwined in your story Morgan that I forgot the reason I'm here. Now giving it thought, this may be an excellent forum for you to voice this very concern."

"What are you referring to?" Morgan asks with less anger and more curiosity.

"A graduate advisor is having an informal get together at

his home and he has invited as many male Negro students as will come. I was just telling Robert about it and now am inviting you."

"What kind of get together is it?" Morgan questions.

"A gathering of likeminded individuals to discuss common ideas like the apparent injustice placed on you by this Dr. of Philosophy, Dr. Platt. This would be an excellent topic for discussion. What to do if the faculty members are against you and show signs of racism, favoritism, or blatant disrespect?"

"Every sentiment you mentioned is what burns in my heart. When is this meeting and who will be in attendance?" Morgan asks, still visibly disheveled. Morgan is upset to the degree that his physical appearance is strikingly abnormal for such a neatly fit individual. Morgan wears a bowtie almost every day. He feels that it says a lot about his character. I don't know how true that is but Morgan has worn a bowtie since I met him in school years ago. If nothing else, he definitely stands out. Not so much here at Cornell, but his neat nature does say a lot about him. I didn't think he would be as rigid once he came here to the campus and settled in. Yet here he is, upset and angry... and neat. This time however, it's different. His hair is neat but his clothes are rambled. His bowtie is untied and hanging loosely around his neck, giving the impression that it will fall to the ground at the slightest gust of wind. His sleeves are rolled up, one to his elbow and the other just past the watch on his wrist. His shirt collar is open and I can tell he's been sweating. He isn't exactly the picture perfect idea of the Cornell intellectual elite. "When is this meeting and who's going to be there? Who will be there to moderate? I certainly will be in attendance!" Morgan says.

421 North Albany Street is a large house with a wide porch and shudders outside the second floor windows. When Roy and I visited Ithaca in '93, I noticed many of the homes with this familiar make up. The door at the end of the porch is already open and I'm sure that's due to this afternoon's unseasonably warm temperature. Due to the meeting

activities of the evening, we're welcome to enter in our own accord I'm certain. Still, I peek inside and walk in slowly, searching for some form of invitation.

"Henry my friend!" A jovial Vertner calls my name. "Welcome! Welcome!"

I laugh at the notion that Vertner is welcoming me into a home that he neither owns nor resides in. "Good afternoon sir, how are you?"

"I'm at my best!" He says back with a laugh. "How are you?"

"Good. Very well. Very anxious about this meeting."

"I think we all are. Do you know the owner of the house Mr. Newton?" He asks.

"I have yet to have the privilege. You know him?"

"I met him a moment ago along with another fellow..." As he is speaking, another student enters the common area from an adjoining room connected through a swinging wood door. He is followed by an older gentleman who smiles as he notices me."

"Oh welcome sir! Please come in." The older man places a tray on the table and extends a hand toward me. He smiles even wider as I take his hand as he introduces himself. "My name is Edward Newton and this is my home. I'm excited about meeting everyone invited and about tonight's agenda."

"My name is Henry Arthur Callis and I'm from Binghamton."

"Binghamton! Good! Good! Have you met Messrs. Tandy and Tompkins?" He asks.

"I know Vertner Tandy. We met on campus but I haven't..." as I'm speaking, the other student comes forward. He was helping Mr. Newton carry a tray into the room. His tray contains cheese and crackers which he has placed down on the table next to Mr. Newton's tray which holds another delicacy.

"Hello Henry, I'm George. George Tompkins. I'm a first year as well." George shakes my hand. He has an awkward smile. He is a confident looking fellow yet has a weak handshake.

46

"Nice to meet you George." Before my pleasantries with George end, three more men walk into the house behind where I'm standing. "Nathaniel, it's good to see you. I'm glad you mentioned this to me." I say to him as I turn around.

Nathaniel takes my hand. "Sure. Glad you could make it Henry. Hello George." Nathaniel and George are already acquainted obviously as they shake each other's hands.

"Good evening Nathaniel." George says.

Nathaniel then introduces the pair that came in with him. "This is Morgan Phillips and Robert Ogle. Meet George Tompkins." Vertner and Mr. Newton join the introductions as well when another gentleman emerges from another adjoining room that I hadn't noticed. This fellow is obviously not a freshman and yet not as old as Mr. Newton by far.

"Gentlemen!" He proclaims proudly. This must be Mr. Poindexter that lives here. "It's good to see we're all coming together on one accord and under one roof. Welcome! Welcome!" He smiles, but his countenance remains firm and constant. "We would like to get started but I want to wait a few minutes for those who were invited that have yet to arrive." With that, he begins to personally make acquaintance with those he hasn't met. First Robert and Morgan, then me. "Hello sir, thank you so much for coming out. You are?
"Henry Arthur Callis from Binghamton."

"Henry from Binghamton. I'm C.C. Poindexter, welcome to my home. Henry, are you familiar with a family by the name of Daughtry from the Binghamton area?"

"Yes actually. Rev. Lynn Daughtry knows my father well. They've shared the pulpit on occasion." Rev. Daughtry is a Baptist preacher and dad is African Methodist Episcopalian yet their fiery styles are very similar.

"Well look at that. I stayed with the Daughtrys for three months. Not in Binghamton though but in New Paltz. They have a home there where the Reverend takes care of a much smaller congregation during the summer months. He's a dedicated fellow as he would travel back and forth to preach in Binghamton as well." At that, two more students enter and C.C. politely excuses himself. He shakes one student's hand as if he knows him and allows that student to introduce the other gentleman. A gentleman I know well... George Kelley.

They share a laugh as Mr. Newton joins their small circle. He whispers a few words to C.C. who acknowledges and turns to face the majority of us.

"Gentlemen, let's begin," he says. "Please feel free to eat at your leisure. The men's facility is through that door and on the left if needed. Please take a seat and we can begin."

I make my way toward Vertner and sit near him. He seems to be the one who knows the least amount of men in attendance. I don't believe he knows anyone here outside of his young friendship with me.

"Good evening fellows." C.C. begins. Everyone replies with a baritone, "Good evening."

"As some of you may know, my name is Charles C. Poindexter but I'd rather be known as C.C. I am a graduate student at the University. I concentrate in the school of agronomy." He breathes but his pause seems more of a stop point for all to reference the magnitude of his introduction so far. Graduate student. I welcome everyone here this afternoon to this meeting. Before we delve into the purpose for this gathering and begin with ideas, I would like for each of us to stand and state your name and possibly where they are hailing from. The more we meet the more we will hopefully familiarize ourselves with at least our first names and definitely our faces. If we can start to my right... oh wait, before I start with you sir, let me have the honor of introducing to you Mr. Edward Newton who owns this residence and was very eager and anxious when I approached him with the idea of tonight's meeting. Thank you sir." Mr. Newton smiles and waves as we clap for him in unison.

C.C. resumes "Now you sir." C.C. takes his seat.

This is the young man that C.C. spoke with right after he was talking to me. They already know one another. This gentleman introduced C.C. to George. "Good evening everyone." We once again chime in with a good evening. "My name is Charles Henry Chapman and I'm a first year student from Carynga County." What a coincidence, his name is Henry as well. Charles is undoubtedly the most serious looking person I've met since I've been in Ithaca, professors withstanding. Actually, only a few professors. This Messr. Chapman holds the demeanor of a judge handing down a justly ruled guilty verdict.

"I must interrupt Charles," C.C. says smiling as he turns toward the group, "we joke with each other often because our names are the same. So do not confuse the two C.C.s of the group if you can help it."

Charles smiles as does everyone else. "Maybe one day we can switch identities and I can be the graduate student." Charles' smile is so welcoming, otherwise he is in deep thought and contemplating something. Anything.

"How about that?" C.C. adds.

Charles takes his seat. George is next to stand.

"Hello brothers, my name is George Biddle Kelley and I bring you greetings from Troy. I attended the Rensselear Polytechnic Institute and now am here at Cornell."

"Wow," Vertner says, "so formal." He lightly laughs at his own joke. His smile remains as he stands and George sits.

"Vertner Woodson Tandy here. I too am a transfer student to Cornell but form the Tuskegee Institute in the great state of Alabama." Vertner's introduction speaks volumes about him as a person. This is truly a fun-loving chap with a lot of zest. I'm glad to have made his acquaintance in particular.

"Alabama huh? Long way from home." Mr. Newton says.

"Actually sir, not as far. I'm not from Alabama, I'm from the greater state of Kentucky. I just went to Alabama to attend the Institute in the south.

"Oh, very well," Mr. Newton adds with a smile.

"Good evening gents. My name, as some of you may know, is Henry Arthur Callis. I'm from Binghamton, NY and I'm pleased to be counted in the company."

Next is George Tompkins. He stands. "Hello everyone. George Tompkins and I too am very pleased to be here. I had no idea what this meeting would consist of but I am certainly glad that I was invited."

"So there's two Charles' and two Georges!" Mr. Newton proclaims. "Interesting."

"I suppose so." C.C. says. "Two Georges."

Next is Nathaniel. "Hello, Nathaniel Allison Murray from

Washington, DC." He sits.

"Morgan Phillips, also from Washington, DC."

"Wow, a few from the capital!" Mr. Newton excitedly says.

"Robert Harold Ogle from Washington also." This makes Mr. Newton and everyone else laugh.

"This can be a meeting of Congress or the Supreme Court, only with Negro constituents!" Mr. Newton jokes.

"Indeed!" That is why we've gathered gentlemen." C.C. regains control. "We've come together in unison tonight to begin to make steps toward change. We as Negroes may never be able to don the robes of the Supreme Court. Why not create awareness within our race for a support system right here on campus for students to have as a resource and be able to draw from?" Mr. Newton stands and quietly leaves the room. C.C. continues. "Gentlemen, I've witnessed many things in my time here." He pauses as if he is pondering his next statement. "The one most poignant and fresh in my mind is the disappearance of many Negro students who once were listed on the role here on campus. With no support system in place, these students or even you sitting here tonight have no definitive guarantee if obstacles arise."

"What types of obstacles usually prevent these students from matriculation?" Vertner asks directly.

"Sometimes there are financial problems that arise. There is no aid available for students who face financial challenges. More often are problems with grades and classes. Students do have the option of consulting with professors or graduate assistants like myself. The cases that I've seen where students have approached me personally have all come too late. By the time I make some attempt to assist, the situation is beyond repair. We have to set up a literary or study group of some kind where we can pour into our students."

Mr. Newton returns with a cup of coffee. He takes his seat.

"Mr. Poindexter, when you..."

"Please, call me C.C. I know it will take some time for us to remember each other's names." C.C. says to me.

"Certainly." I say. "When you say a study group, what is the underlying sentiment or purpose of a group where everyone's studies vary depending on their individual concentration?"

"Good question Henry and that is the exact strength of a literary society. See, with a variety of backgrounds and concentrations, we can offer so much more to students coming behind us. We also have strength in unity in that we can confront injustices that may face each of us in our experiences."

Morgan stands. "If I may, I would like to share an experience that falls along the lines of what you're speaking to C.C."

"Sure, please. Give us your name once again."

"Morgan Phillips."

"Please Morgan, proceed," C.C. advises.

"I have a philosophy class instructed by Dr. Platt. I don't know if you know of him C.C."

"No, I don't."

"Well, the class had an assignment and when mine was corrected and returned to me, my final score was not indicative of my work whatsoever. I approached the professor and his assistant and they all but mocked me and ridiculed my attempt at discussion."

"What did they say?" Vertner asks.

"First, I was made to wait for over twenty minutes. I wouldn't mind waiting if the professor was with another student or busy with class work. The professor and his assistant instead were engaged in casual conversation with one another while I waited." I can see Morgan getting upset as he begins his recount. "Once I was allowed entry into the office, I was treated rudely, spoken to harshly and laughed at by the graduate assistant."

"This professor's name is Dr. Platt you mentioned?" C.C. asks.

"Yes, Dr. Platt." Morgan answers.

"I would be frustrated as well." George Tompkins says.

"I'm sure these situations happen all the time."

"I'm actually surprised we don't hear of this more often." Mr. Newton says before placing his coffee cup down.

"We would if we had a place to vent these feelings." C.C. remarks confidently. "We would hear of discrimination, mistreatment, unfair tactics and the like. We never hear of these things because we've never had a vehicle or organization representative of our needs. Not until this social study club that we are now discussing. That, gentlemen, is what I've called you here for." C.C. seems to have a means of gaining respect through capturing one's attention. His commanding presence is clearly a driving force in his speech, delivery and stance as his words permeate the room. I find it fascinating as I scan the faces of the others in the room to note how attentive each man is on C.C.'s every word. Like me, each man in attendance is contemplating his own contribution to Negro society on Cornell's campus as C.C. drives his motivating point. That is, to encourage each of us to band together for the common good.

C.C. pauses before he moves on. He looks around the room either for comments or questions. His approach to group discussion is reminiscent of Reverend Henry Jesse Callis, 'Look at as many colored folk in the fast as you can. Show yourself strong."

"With a literary society," C.C. continues, "we can set in motion a movement toward the fair and ethical treatment of colored students. We need to organize ourselves first, setting monthly or bimonthly meetings. From there, we can set our organization's sights on correcting wrongs and laying a firm foundation for other students coming behind to stand on."

George Tompkins is the next to speak. "C.C., so it is our understanding that you wish to establish a social study group? I see the possibilities and I think it's a grand idea." George answers his own question before allowing C.C. to.

George Kelley, the other George comments. "With a club having a focus on study, I don't see how that can address the needs of a student such as the Negro who faces so many varying faces on the campus of an all-White institution. It would seem that as our emphasis is geared at assisting the Negro at overcoming barriers in the classroom, we are missing the point in pressing him toward excellence in other areas."

George's statement may have taken a few back... not me. I actually had the same thought cross my mind a bit earlier in the discussion while C.C. was describing his ideas of the organization. George's challenge seems to widen the possibilities for advancement as it would encompass a group more fitting to the overall person, not just the literary one.

"Although I am in full agreement, as I assume we all in attendance are, with the efforts at unifying and coming together for the common good, the vehicle is what I question." George finishes.

"What other type of group are you proposing then? I haven't considered another and don't know of any truly fitted to our purposes." C.C. asks.

"A fraternity." George's words, these two simple words, resound in the air as if he spat them in slower motion due to their heavy weight.

We were already gazing at George anticipating his reply. Yet, none were quite prepared for the answer he presented. No one including myself or Mr. Newton who is now smiling or C.C. Poindexter, arms folded, lips pressed together, contemplating his next chess move. 'Show yourself strong.'

"A fraternity?" C.C. mocks more than asks, not in a disrespectful tone, but mockingly nonetheless. "A fraternity is certainly not along the lines of what we need created. That serves no purpose for the collegiate Negro. Instead you need to face the challenges facing each and every one of you, to take it upon yourselves the earnest responsibility of one another in unity, scholastic achievement, and advancement."

For the first time this evening, C.C. refers to the group as yourselves and not including himself in his description. Probably a mere oversight. However construed, the idea for social study club and the idea for fraternity simultaneously were born that evening. Like siblings joined by blood but separated by ideology, as Cain and Abel, the evening ends with these two opinions on everyone's mind, one contrasting the other.

"I'm thankful the three of us have this chance to meet and

discuss." I say to both Henry and George Kelley. "I have an idea we are all of one mind and one accord since the meeting."

"I believe you're right." Henry says.

"I've made my sentiments known." George says. "I believe everyone is aware of how I feel concerning the matter." I smile at George. I admire his candor and admitted courage.

"You know, because I've worked with and seen Poindexter in a classroom setting, it's more unnerving for me to state what you stated, although I sense what you're stating deep inside."

"That's the proposition Nathaniel," George says matter-of-factly. "That if we are honest with ourselves and what our intentions are, we have to voice that. You know, as does Henry and probably others, that as a fraternity we have a foundation to stand on. I've researched it and thought about it. Contemplating it even. Seen it from close proximity. It would revolutionize this campus for the Negro!" George's excitement is contagious.

How likely though is this notion? A fraternity for Negroes. Something that, it seemed from our meeting, Mr. Poindexter is the least bit interested in. "Think about this fact George, C.C. Poindexter became president of our club. He serves the group as our leader. What is the proposal for changing or modifying his view on the organization's totality and usefulness in one capacity more than the other?"

George smiles. "That is where our good friend Henry proves to be essential. With Henry serving as secretary and in close quarters with C.C. on the development of the club, with input from all of course, we have all we need to travel the road of change and true unity through brotherhood, not mere acquaintance."

"Interesting concept." I say.

"It is." Henry chimes in. "Yet one not to be taken lightly, but observed closely. In my research at the fraternity house, I've found the gentlemen there quite helpful in offering information and answering questions. Within their reason of course. All helpful however."

"The same with me," George adds. "Curiosity is the main reason I work at the house."

"That and the obvious need for financial assistance." I jokingly add. Both George's and Henry's laugh tell me their admittance to the fact as well as the humor found in it.

"I certainly cannot debate with you there Nathaniel but I've learned a lot in the process and am thankful to have the experience. At least to my better understanding. The desire is great. Not merely to mimic what they have with their campus events and game but to begin something monumental. Something revolutionary. A place, a home for Negro men at Cornell for years to come and after."

George Biddle Kelley is a man of sure expressions. It's clear that when he knows what he is in desire of, he at least knows how to voice it confidently. As he speaks, there are no expressions of insincerity on his face and his demeanor is strong. George possesses the face of a youth but the ideology of a man well beyond our years.

"I thought it a very interesting and monumental event, this Niagara Conference." Henry adds. "Your words George bring me to thoughts of the gathering. Imagine the thoughts of the Negro's greatest intellectual minds converging in a place to discuss the state of the race and the politics or lack thereof within. It's encouraging to know that on our behalf there are discussions geared toward the challenges facing the Negro. These men gathered with a sense of unity and purpose. It's in the same spirit that we must galvanize our efforts in making this society of ours a landmark."

With all the students and friends that I've made in growing up in Washington, I've never met individuals quite like these new comrades at Cornell. Henry, Vertner, C.C., both Georges, these brothers are positive thinkers seemingly thinking of others first and the common good. With my anticipation of college life and all that this journey would afford me, I never considered the structuring of such a social study club. For one, I never imagined the extreme necessity. Yet, according to C.C. and the others, the time is now and time is of the essence. Many others have fallen by the wayside, partially because a club such as this has not been set in motion.

"Henry, what are your honest opinions of C.C.?"

"He seems to be a great man of insight. To witness what he has over the years and see the need for a society to study and ensure the Negro of his place in this institution is grand."

"I agree. How about you?"

George adds "I wholeheartedly agree. I believe C.C. has the same vision we all share. The injustice Morgan offered the group is one story among many. Unfair treatment is probably the law of the land here and there is no accountability on the part of the guilty. How do we create a fair and equitable experience in a system already rooted not necessarily in our failure, but not entirely for our success either?"

"You have to start small," Henry adds. "Just as we are. These situations will not change overnight. They can change however. That was proven by the Niagara. The meeting had to take place on the other side of the border, but how long will that be the case? At some point, these same discussions will take place on American soil and at some point the cases at Cornell will be brought to the attention of the body at large."

C.C. Poindexter's work space is merely an upgraded version of what all students have. As a graduate student however, he is definitely afforded the office environment and setting and he takes full advantage of that luxury. His papers and documents are neatly arranged and there are books that line his shelf. It's an incredible task in and of itself for him to have read the amount of books that he possesses. I've never met anyone with such a passion for reading, if he has indeed read this many books. The environment is a thinking person's paradise as the quiet is almost loud.

"I remember that you're George Tompkins," he says confidently. He's right. Him remembering my full name isn't impressive. There were two Georges and two Charles. The other George challenged him to a very small degree. Of course he remembers this George.

"Yes. I hope this isn't a bad time."

"No, no. Please come in and sit down. It's good to see you George." he says invitingly. "What brings you by? I'm more surprised you aren't out on the campus with today's weather."

"It's very fair out indeed. I thought to come by however and talk if you had the time."

"Sure. I can most certainly accommodate. What crosses your mind?"

"I just wanted to commend you on your efforts from the other night. I know this idea of a social club must have been on your mind for some time. I think it shows great courage and foresight to call to arms the group as you have."

C.C. doesn't smile as I thought he would. His approval warrants much more effort it seems and to work toward pleasing him is definitely a desire because of his disposition and nature. I look up to C.C. in the sense that I would like to reach back and help students coming after me when I'm in the position he is in. I'm sure he'll be proud of the social study club in years to come when we've archived exams, documentations, study materials, and resources and have a definitive home for the Negro who wishes to advance his studies. Literature as a backdrop and advancement as a forefront is a unique calling for the Negro. Such a notion would probably be deemed futile at best by most institutions. All the more reason to forge ahead and document these efforts.

"I cannot take the credit for the hard work and determination that will be put forth by the group at large George. Although I appreciate your sentiments. The sentiments of the group rang strong that evening and it pleased me greatly as to the outcome in both attendance and acceptance. It's been on my mind ever since and I've thought of nothing else."

"What are the next plans?" I ask.

"Our next meeting is set for next week Saturday, November 11th. I spoke with Henry Callis and he has notified some of the others. If you come into contact with any of the men that attended, please do the same until we are all made aware. I have research documents that I'll be bringing to that meeting. Maybe they'll be useful to someone in their studies."

"Are your materials strictly for this department though?"

I look around his space again and notice he owns books of all types; answering my own question.

"I've actually amassed several books either from friends who've gone on past Cornell or my personal studies. I make it a point to be a fan of literature and the pen so I collect a lot. I have even more at my home."

"Incredible."

"I can show you my extensive book collection the next time you're over at the house. If you would like to explore in reading."

"Certainly. I would check out a book a month from you!" Now C.C. laughs and leans back in his chair. His laughter however, what I was searching for, is both good and bad. Good in the sense that I've struck a closer tie with him in the mere fact that my statement loosened him to the point of an outward expression. Bad in the sense that I am not a reader like that by any whimsical thought. Now I've assigned myself the task of borrowing a book from him on various occasions just to keep my word. I now have to possibly read them all!

"I'll be somewhat of a library for you then. I will have to make sure I catalog your entries." C.C. says smiling.

"Most certainly." I reply and wishing I could take back the entire thing.

There's silence before C.C. breaks it with his next statement, an interrogative one. "George, are you familiar with the literary critic William Ferris?"

"No I'm not familiar." I cross my legs to try and seem more relaxed.

"Ferris is a strong critic to Booker T. Washington and his ideologies." C.C. stands up and searches the shelf behind him for a book. He continues to speak with his back turned toward me. "Ferris is actually one of my favorite critics. I, like Ferris, oppose Washington's small minded views on Negro education."

"Small minded?" I ask the question before taking the time to think of what I'm asking. Now it may seem that I'm not familiar, or as familiar with Booker T. as C.C. is. To an extent, I'm not as it would almost be sheer blasphemy to refer to Booker as anything other than scholarly and a man well beyond his years in thought and character. How can one not agree with Booker T.?

C.C. turns around to face me. "Washington feels that the common school education is good enough for a Negro. That's why he was denounced at the Bethel Literary Society in Washington. A decision I wholeheartedly agree with. See, that's the reason we need a literary society here. To make such blazing accusations and be correct in our claims!" C.C. laughs and I with him. He had taken a manuscript from the shelf that I didn't see him pick up. "Listen to the words of Ferris as he describes Washington." C.C. opens the manuscript to read. " 'He grovels in the mud and mire of Southern prejudice to gratify an itching palm and please the White man in the South.' What a startling accusation! See, the more Washington speeches about our need to till the land and be farm hands, the White have no confidence in the higher education process of the Negro."

"I see what you mean." I say.

"That, George, is why literature is vital. We have to make a mark on the minds of Negro men and women. We must start here in our homes first."

C.C. is not a conventional thinker at all. I, like most people I know with any level of intelligence, see Booker T. Washington in an exemplary light. Who wouldn't? Maybe W.E.B. DuBois but his ideologies have signs of weakness as well. For C.C. to outright oppose the man and align with a strong critic shows strength of character. An impressive display of character to say the least. The type of tremendous character built for leadership.

To think that Morgan almost passed this evening up is incredible. Personally, no headache on earth could've kept me away. A coming out of sorts for the new class of students at Cornell. This is a fantastic occasion, one that it seems others think highly of as well. There are more students here then I've seen in one gathering since coming to Cornell.

"I owe you a great debt for dragging me out of the room." Morgan says. He does owe me because had he slept through this, he might've hated himself as well as me. He undoubtedly has looked around the room at the gathering, still growing, in the living room of the Moore family.

"Yes you do owe me and I will collect." I say laughingly.

"Collect the... information... for me Robert... and I will... make... certain... I retrieve..." Morgan falls asleep mid-sentence.

"Oh no, wake up! Let's go! I can tell you're fast asleep and in another world because you're speaking of information and I told you this is a social gathering. No information. Just fellowship. So wake up and come along!"

I pull Morgan by his arm which by means of connection, drags his torso off the mattress. He probably would hit the floor hard if it had not been for me holding his arm.

"Robert! What are you doing?"

"I told you that we are going to this event this evening! I owe it to you because I gave you my word. Besides, who wants to go to a social event alone?"

"Alright! Alright! I'm up!" Morgan says as his once limp arms are now supporting half of his upper body in push up position. He struggles to his feet, rubs his temples, and starts to get dressed. "This better be worth it Bob! My head is pounding!"

"This night is well worth it!" Morgan says as he bites onto a carrot stick. "Well worth it indeed. Oh, there's Nathaniel."

"Where?"

Morgan gestures toward the doorway and I notice Nathaniel being greeted by Ms. Irene Moore, the hostess of the evening and resident of the house. The Moore home is owned by Henry Moore, one of the most popular men in all Ithaca. Several social gatherings are held here each season, this one being the welcoming to the new students of Cornell. The word spread quickly on campus regarding this event and it seems a lot of students took them up on their invitation. I thought I had just about met all the new faces to Ithaca but I was mistaken. Many of these students I don't recall at all.

"Good evening gentlemen." Nathaniel says as he approaches.

"How are you Nathaniel?"

"Fine Morgan, thanks for asking. Yourself?"

I answer for Morgan. "He doesn't want to be here."

"Not true! I didn't want to come but upon arrival, those thoughts have departed." Morgan returns laughing.

"I'm sure they have." Nathaniel says as he looks around the room. "Do you know any of these new students?"

"Some." I say. "There are a few faces that I don't recognize."

"There's George. George Kelley." Nathaniel notes.

"I hadn't even seen him. Yes, there he is."

"Maybe I'll greet him. Will you two remain here?" Nathaniel asks.

In looking in George's direction, I can't help but notice two young ladies who are standing in George's general vicinity. Amidst everyone in attendance, talking, eating, mingling... amidst individuals entering the house and leaving the house... amidst people I know, people I've seen but don't know, people I simply haven't seen... amidst my amusing conversation with Morgan... amidst my studies and exams so far... amidst everything I know about Ithaca, the Singletons with their keen and mannerly ways... amidst all family I remember at home in Washington, all friends from prestigious M School and everyone I've ever laid my eyes on.. I've never seen anyone as beautiful as the young lady I am staring at right now. At this moment, I can no longer hear Nathaniel or Morgan. I don't hear the buzz of conversation about school, campus life, how are yous, nice to meet yous, how have you beens. She turns and looks my way and I freeze, even as she freezes when our eyes meet. For the split second that we stare at one another, the glances are locked with a lock that only one key can open. The key of knowledge of self. As soon as you acknowledge within yourself that you are staring at someone, you unlock your gaze and turn away. The question however, which of the locked parties uses the key first?

"Robert... did you hear me?" Morgan asks.

"Huh? What did you say?" Apparently Morgan owns a

similar key.

"I was asking if you wanted to join Nathaniel and me in greeting George."

"No." I reply. "You go ahead. I'll speak to you in a minute."

With my attention totally subverted from Morgan, Nathaniel, George, President Shurman, President Roosevelt, or anyone else, I gaze back at the two young ladies and begin to walk in their direction. She notices me because she giggles with her friend and tries her best to not make me the object of her full attention. Instead, she gives the impression as to not notice me coming her way.

"Good evening, my name is Robert."

"Hello Robert," her friend says abruptly "my name is Chase."

It's clear that my intentions are not necessarily to meet Chase. Manners being what they are, I smile a welcoming smile and extend my hand to take hers. "It's a pleasure to meet you." Now my true mission. "And you are?"

"Helen Moore."

"Helen Moore." The name slides off of my tongue effortlessly. "I can't say that I've seen you on campus before. What are you studying and why have you been in hiding?"

"She's studying business." Chase blurts out with a giggle.

"The fact is you won't see me on campus. I don't attend Cornell. I'm a senior majoring in business at Ithaca high school."

"Oh wait a minute," I hadn't made the connection, "you said your last name is Moore. This is your family's residence."

"Yes, I live here." she replies.

"I see." It makes sense now. I know for certain had she been a Cornell student, I would've seen her by now and tried my best to make her acquaintance. "This is a lovely home you have here." I'm not quite sure if this was the best thing to offer. It's not as if she owns the house.

"You would have to credit my grandfather for that." she says.

"Henry Moore?" I ask, already knowing the answer.

"Yes! You know of my grandfather?"

"Everyone does. All of Ithaca. All of New York. All of the world."

When Helen Moore laughs, its springtime sunshine during a thunderstorm.

"Robert, what are you studying in school?" Chase asks. I had forgotten she was standing there.

"Uh... I'm..."

"Didn't think we'd find you here old boy." Morgan walks up from behind me, slapping his hand on my shoulder. He'll probably embarrass me in front of Helen unless I take the lead. At the same time, I must thank him later for saving me from Chase's question which ultimately would've been my downfall had I not known the answer. With Helen's beauty as my focus, I probably don't know the answer to most simple questions.

"Morgan, Nathaniel. This is Chase and Helen. Helen is of the Moore family and lives here." Taking the lead.

"Pleasure to meet you." Chase says with an even bigger smile then when she met me.

"Pleased to meet you too," Nathaniel says. "Are you new students as well?"

"No, we both attend Ithaca high school. We're seniors though." Chase adds the fact that although they are both in high school and not on our level, they soon will be in a matter of months. It doesn't make any difference to me in the least bit. Helen is someone I would like to get to know better and as Morgan says, this evening is 'well worth it' if I do.

Charles Chapman seems a man of few words but words carefully chosen and spoken with much dignity nonetheless. He intrigued me at the meeting at 42 and I made it a point to set aside time to meet the man and ask him a few questions about himself. His café is small with an iron cast stove in the middle of the room. He is sitting at a table in the far corner reading and writing. He doesn't even notice as I approach but he looks up as my shadow casts down on his paperwork.

"Vertner!"

"How are you Charles? Just thought I would stop by and see the place and get a chance to chat." I say.

Charles smiles and starts to move papers to make room for me. "Please have a seat."

"I'm not interrupting am I? I can come back at another time." I reply as I take the seat nonetheless.

"Oh no, its fine." Charles says. "Just doing a little reading, that's all. What brings you by? Would you like a fresh cup of coffee?"

"Sure. Black please."

Without another word, Charles is up and off. I take a moment to look around his establishment. Quaint tables and chairs. Two white students are talking of the news of the day at another table. Simple brick edifice. What's impressive is that a freshman student in college is able to run a café. He returns quickly with my cup of coffee.

"Do all your customers get served this quickly or am I special because we're new friends?"

"Have to keep the customers coming back. Good business. You are a friend Vertner so there is extra care in your cup." I laugh more than he does.

"How does one amass a business? Well, better question, how does one start a business venture while in college's first semester?" I ask before I sip.

"Better question than that Vertner, what is that crazy hat you're wearing?" I had noticed him look up at me and at my head and honestly I had forgotten I was wearing my hat. I'd forgotten my manners and hadn't removed my hat upon entering the establishment. "Oh this?" I say as I remove it. "This is my straw hat. You don't like it? It's the fashion craze in Kentucky."

"I don't know how popular it will find itself in New York my friend." His straight expression is hard to judge whether he is pulling my leg or very serious. I laugh however as I place my hat over my knee.

"So back to my question."

"Oh yes. Well you have to understand what's good for us. We can't expect anything from anyone and anticipate anyone helping us. Our plight is our plight and whatever is made of it is what you make of it."

"I understand that wholeheartedly." I say.

Charles continues. "For me in particular, I've been of this mind for some time. Have you heard, well maybe you haven't, but have you heard of the North Carolina Mutual and Provident Association?" He asks me.

"North Carolina? I've only been through the state. Never stopped in my travels." I say with a laugh. Charles doesn't laugh yet continues.

"There are Negro businessmen from the Durham area who have begun enterprises sparked by the eloquence of Booker T. Washington."

I smile a big smile and place my cup down. "Is that so?"

"Indeed. They have patterned themselves after his replica of the Negro pulling himself up and making it for himself. They are a group solely motivated to live out the meaning and defining vision of Washington and are quite successful at it thus far."

"I'm sure Dr. Washington would be happy to hear that news. I'll be sure to inform him of such a group when we next speak."

Finally Charles smiles as he leans back in his chair and folds his arms. "So you're going to notify Booker T. personally?"

"I sure will. The next time I'm down at Skegee, I will."

"Wait a minute." He leans forward in his chair and unfolds his arms. "You did say that you attended Tuskegee Institute didn't you?" He asks curiously.

"Yes I did say that." I answer. Now it seems that the tables have turned. What was first my interest in getting to know Charles may have now become his interest in getting to know me, now that he realizes my associate mentor.

"You know Washington personally?"

"Yes." I say proudly, "he served as my mentor while I was

enrolled there."

"Well isn't that just incredible. I must say I admire the man for his stand, his position and for his calling to the yard of men who look to better themselves. I'm very impressed with his repertoire." Charles states.

"Most are." I add. "He's a great thinker and a dedicated worker in all he puts himself to. I'm sure he'd be impressed with you. A first year student with a venture such as this." I look around the room again. "Maybe he can have coffee here some time." Charles laughs this time. "You must be very busy between your studies and keeping business."

"Yes, and I own a brickyard as well." Charles adds.

"You do? Goodness Charles do you sleep a wink?"

"Not when there's work to be done Vertner. Not when the call is out and there is work to be done."

I'll drink to that!

This time I'm the first to arrive which gives me ample time to state my claim to C.C. before others begin to come in themselves. By purposely arriving early, I hope to engage Professor Poindexter and ascertain his thought process and vision while detailing where my energies will be exerted. This order that he has initiated by a simple call to meet has sparked a generous amount of afterthought and consideration not only by me but by others who attended I'm sure.

The house is much more quiet this evening. When I arrived last time there was a conversation taking place inside and the door was open. This time, I knock on the door and C.C. opens it.

"Good evening George, you're rather early." He looks at his watch.

"I know. I believe in being more than punctual." C.C. laughs and steps aside to let me in.

"That's a great bit of character to have then," he adds,

"I apologize that I don't already have a beverage or food available but I wasn't expecting anyone this early."

"No need to apologize. I have more interest in talking to you however, another reason I decided to come a little before the group."

"Sure. Let's sit down then."

Mr. Newton enters the living area accompanied by two ladies, apparently his wife and daughter. "Good evening sir." He says smiling with an outstretched hand.

"Sir, you remember George. George Kelley." C.C. says as we both stand.

"Yes indeed. Welcome back."

"Thank you sir." I say as I take his hand cordially. "Nice to visit you again."

"Please allow me to introduce my wife Lula and Florence our daughter."

Mrs. Newton smiles as she delicately takes my hand. Florence greets me with a pleasant hello. As the mother daughter pair prepare to leave, C.C. says a few words to Florence, none that I can hear or make out and she smiles. Then the two are off to their destination.

"Can I get you anything George? Hot tea maybe?" Mr. Newton asks.

"No sir, I'm fine thank you."

"Okay then." Mr. Newton turns toward C.C. "I will be in the kitchen preparing."

"Thank you sir." C.C. replies.

C.C. and I sit back down to resume, or initiate, our conversation.

"Yes George, now what exactly did you care to talk about?"

"I want to capture your vision and mindset on the objectives of this group. What prompted you to action, besides the aforementioned items you expressed in the initial meeting? Are there underlying thoughts or motives here? And if so, how can we work together to see visions coming together?"

C.C. is a thinker. His facial expression shows deep thought as he ponders my questions and prepares the best response. He is an intellectual. I'm expecting a well-rounded answer, more than the reasons he indicated in our first meeting. Although noble indeed, I would believe that further research will indicate the real directive. Hopefully those reasons will coincide with mine.

"George, I'm glad you asked am I'm also pleased you thought enough to come speak to me directly." He pauses before he continues. "The missing link, if you will, is education. Not merely the notion that we are members of the college educated thus afforded more than other brethren. Additionally, we have to educate ourselves. More than what this society of Cornell will educate us. Within our personal society, we have to read. We have to study. We have to offer. We have to supply. In no other capacity can we make a mark on the minds of individuals following in our footsteps and searching for directives." He shifts in his chair as if he is ready to truly expound. "This notion that higher education is not fit for Negroes is fallible at best. We must as men forge ahead and relieve ourselves of such notions and tackle the obstructions that lie in the road ahead. There is no apology acceptable for ignorance when the mantle to eradicate it has been placed on our shoulders."

"What about brotherhood?" I interrupt. "What about creating a home for ourselves as men where we can embrace the vision that you are speaking of and also find strength in a fraternal bond?"

The interruption and question lead to an abrupt silence. C.C. was on track with his speech, his motivation dissertation. I, however, broke his momentum of sorts and now he requires time to recalculate and ponder his thoughts.

He begins with a smile. "Still on this notion are we George?"

"Unwavering."

"There is no documentation anywhere of a successful Negro fraternity. It's certainly not our mandate to imitate what we've seen instituted by our fellow university mates. If anything, our challenge is of a much stronger intellectual caliber. Our call is not to a fraternity or some form of organization. Our call is to a literary society. A literary society." He repeats for emphasis sake. "Where we can offer ourselves and our fellow students valuable resources and equipment to further both ours and their education."

"Notwithstanding your notion sir, but we can accomplish that still keeping with the formation of a fraternal organization. These concepts are not foreign to those in fraternity, yet they..."

"Prove that George. I challenge you to prove that and I'm certain you're unable to because of your limited access."

"Sir, I wait in one of the largest houses on campus. I talk to those men on almost a daily basis."

"How much are they willing to actually share with you? How much are they going to tell you, you being the help in the house?" He asks rather sternly. "That is a secret society George... a secret society. They by no means mean us any service."

"I'm not suggesting they intend us any service or disservice. I'm stating the fact that I do have access to more than you may be aware of and the notion of an organization exclusively for us is not absurd. As a matter of fact, it is of some interest to many of the same men who were here last evening."

"I truly beg to differ." C.C. says flatly. "It's more of a renegade idea with no foreseeable future and no foundation."

His final statement is followed by another awkward moment of silence. I certainly didn't intent to meet with C.C. before the meeting in order to argue with him. With two viewpoints, both held passionately, debate escalates and stalemate ensues.

"We can determine the level of favorability quite easily actually. It simply needs to be brought to head once everyone arrives and possibly brought to a vote."

C.C. responds quickly. "A vote? As president of the literary society, I'm not going to bring to a vote the possibly dissipation of our group."

We're now both interrupted by Charles Chapman's entrance through the front door. The door was left open by

Mrs. Newton and Florence when they left. My discussion with C.C. will have to be tabled to another time as I'm sure he is now not willing to entertain me with the meeting of the society. At least he understands that my motives are not merely fleeting.

"Good evening gentlemen." Charles says as C.C. and I stand to greet him.

"How are you sir?" I ask.

"Fine. Very well thank you."

"Charles, I'm glad you're here a little early. I would like to ask you a question. How do you feel about a fraternity? I mean, would you be willing to support this effort stronger as a literary society as proposed or as some sort of fraternity?" What an unfair question for C.C. to ask!

I look at C.C. totally surprised at his overly leading question and condescending tone. His question of Charles is not only surprising but in all fairness to me, disrespectful. Before I can voice my disdain for the question, or provide at least an explanation as to the awkward question, Charles begins to answer.

"I'm more in favor of the literary society." Charles says. "I thought it was a well thought out idea when I'd heard it."

C.C. doesn't bask in this minor victory. He instead proceeds with business as usual as Mr. Newton walks in with a tray of food and C.C. joins the efforts to assist.

As it could even be imaginable, Helen is prepared far better than our first meeting... and our second meeting.

"Good afternoon Robert." she says politely.

I bow and tip my hat like a gentleman. Purposely exaggerating the movements though causes Helen to laugh a little. Helen's laugh, especially her little laugh, will brighten any day especially this dreary one. From the look of the sky, it may open at any moment and pour God's waterfall worth of rain. Nevertheless, we've decided to take a walk this afternoon and nothing could keep us away from that appointment.

"How are you?" I ask as we begin our walk.

"Very well and how are you?"

"I'm pleased to see you again."

"That is the exact thing you said the last time. I'm beginning to think you have that one line memorized and will use it in all of our future engagements." Helen says laughing.

Her statement is very funny, not for its truth. I actually don't remember what I said exactly when I saw Helen last. I do recall it was hard for me to remember the day of the week and the time of day when I saw her sitting on the front porch. Exactly what I said is a mystery to me. Hence if she reminds me of what was said, I have no choice but to believe it to be so. Her statement is instead funny because if ever I was honest in life, it's with that very statement. I actually am very pleased to see Helen again. Nothing could be truer of my sentiments. So if that is what I said last time, it's because it was true last time. If that is what I say this time, it is certainly because it is true right now. If that is what I will say tomorrow, it will be truer tomorrow than it is today.

"With all honesty Helen, it is good to see you. You've brightened a normally rainy, dreary day."

She smiles at either my statement, my serious tone in delivering it, or both. Regardless, she smiles and looks away bashfully. Awkwardly, we both step into the silence that has pursued, overtaken and now runs before us. In searching for words to break the silence...

"How has your week been? Tell me about college life." she asks.

"Which question would you like for me to answer?" I ask smiling back at her.

"Oh I apologize," she replies nervously, "answer them both." she says more confidently.

"Alright well if I may, I will answer in reverse order than how you inquired."

"Fine." she says smiling.

"College life..." I deem myself more prepared to answer

than I really am. "...let's simply say that it presents challenges to one that one would have never imagined or prepared for. It can be the best of times I'm sure, yet a trying experience at the same time."

"Are you trying to frighten me?" she asks.

"Certainly not. I think my response is more geared toward my personal feelings if anything. Not in general and certainly not to frighten you."

I smile as we pass by a fence and slow our pace. I lean against the fence while turning to face Helen directly. If God has ever created a more beautiful woman, He has certainly hid her from me.

"Did something go terribly wrong for you?" Helen asks me with such concern that I have to think back and reminisce about the very topic of our discussion. My mind had wondered off the path of our discussion and onto the essence of her beauty. I'm sure my immediate look of confusion alerts Helen that her question is not quite understood.

"You were stating that your response was geared toward your own personal feelings. What types of feelings are they?"

"Well," I actually consider telling her. "I don't want to bore you with the inner workings."

"No please. I would like to know."

"Would you really?" I ask. I cannot quite understand why she would want to know, yet I realize it's her not knowing the nature of my statement that drives her curiosity.

"Yes, I would not have asked otherwise now would I?"

I laugh at that one.

"Alright fine. We conducted another meeting of the literary society."

"How nice!" Helen interrupts.

"Wait, let me inform you of what happened before you give accolades." We both laugh, even though my tone begins to indicate that I'm becoming more serious toward actually providing an answer for her questions. "I arrived at the house with Morgan and once we began our discussion a debate ensues. A heated debate."

"Really?" Helen's eyes open up like a child's on Christmas

morning.

"Some of us would like this group to transform into a full fraternity model." I continue. "While the rest wish to remain or rather expound on the program already established by C.C."

"Who?"

"C.C. Poindexter. He's the president of society."

"Yes! I was introduced to him."

"Yes. Great intellectual. Good man. I don't know about his stern views though."

"You don't agree with him?"

"Not really."

"Have you told him that you possibly don't agree with his views?"

"No, I haven't."

"Why not? If you're concerned..."

"It isn't quite that simple Helen."

"It seems to be." she says innocently. "Tell him that you either agree or disagree and move forward."

"C.C. doesn't seem the type to take well to that sort of bluntness. He'd probably rather let individuals fall in line with his suggestions."

"What if his suggestions are not agreed upon by everyone? What if you want something that he doesn't want? Is there a voting in the literary society at all?"

"We spoke... or conducted debate actually about that. The fact is, it seems like we are deadlocked on the issue. Neither side budging but all seem to be open to conversation. I don't know about C.C. on that point, but the others seem willing to at least discuss."

A moment of silence ensues as Helen and I continue walking. She seems to be pondering my statements about the meeting more than I have. Granted, the thing has been on my mind and occupying my thought, but the same thoughts quickly escape me when I see Helen. Any and all thoughts escape... rarely to return. As we approach the trail, I recognize a classmate of mine and I salute.

"Greetings Bob," he gestures.

I nod in his direction and turn my attention back toward Helen. "You were smart to bring your umbrella." I say looking toward the sky.

"You were not as smart I take it."

"Not at all," I say smiling. "Not at all."

Helen opens her umbrella as a light drizzle begins to fall. Recognizing that my hat may not be sufficient if the rain begins to fall violently, I search quickly for a newspaper to hold over my head.

"Maybe we should walk back toward my house." Helen says.

"That's a good idea."

I take a newspaper placed across one of the park benches and open it to cover my head. Upon opening it, I glance across an article that directly catches my attention.

"You can answer my second question now or I guess it would be my first question."

I don't respond to Helen's question nor do I continue walking. I stop... in the third line of the paragraph of the article... and onto the fourth line as if I'm no longer standing with Helen.

"Robert?"

I'm still reading.

"What is it?" Helen asks. Her question brings me immediately back to reality as I hadn't realized that I daydreamed into the article. I look up at Helen and tuck the paper under my arm, forgetting that I was to use it as a shield against the rain.

"I apologize. I saw something here that I must immediately confer with Henry about!"

"Actually gentlemen, I was attempting to close up for the

evening. If it I just a cup of coffee that you're looking for, I can pour one."

"Well actually my boy, I was looking for a little more. Why don't you round up three or four of those hot biscuits and some coffee. Add a cup of hot tea."

The three students laugh, either at the fact that he is attempting to overpower me with his request or the fact that he called me boy. I don't recognize the three. They obviously attend Cornell, probably seniors. Probably privileged. Probably from upstate New York. Definitely arrogant.

I've seen their kind on several occasions. Not so much here in the café. Luckily I don't come across this type of attitude in my establishment. I do know that the underlying sentiment exists amongst many White students and faculty. I am not so certain if those feelings are one sided and not reciprocated from Negro students to an extent.

"Did I not mention that I was closing the establishment down for the evening?" I say. "I can prepare a cup of coffee for each of you but that would be the extent of it as I have already returned my materials to their place."

"What is your name?" The first student addresses me... as if I'm worthy of having some truer sense of worth since I am conversing with him.

"Charles. Charles Chapman."

"Fine Charles. Why don't you run along and gather up whatever items you need and prepare our biscuits and tea."

"Let's leave David. Let him close up his place." another says. This one more than likely feels sorry for me, assuming that I'm placed in an awkward position by his friend David. What neither he nor David realizes is that I've dealt with much worse than witless, White college students. I'm a senior in comparison in my own right and I don't quietly back down. Not for someone who's accomplished so much in short time and has so much to accomplish. I've seen these young boys who are nothing more than college attending farm hands try and secure an upper hand on lowly minded Negroes. Especially the Negro students from the Southern states. These are the ones who will stand for such treatment because they are used to seeing it, used to dealing with it and succumbing, or used to living it and accepting it. The underlying reason is that the arrogant have no one to seize power from because they themselves have been slighted in life and placed in a category of inferiority by someone else. Whether an overbearing father figure, which is more than likely the case in this particular situation or some other dominant individual in their lives. Hence, the need to show power over someone considerably weaker than they, in order to recompense.

The more I make my journey through the educating annals of Cornell University, the more I realize the need to galvanize students like myself, those of the race in small number, heavily outnumbered by our White counterparts. The need is ever so apparent and justifiable. For much more than the small mind, educated yet ignorant lower class of "Davids" of America. Rather, we have to pull together the members of our race who have no problem standing against the wrongs of injustice on any level.

"Gentlemen, nothing would bring me more pleasure then to serve you this evening. If you would allow me, please have a seat so I can retreat the bread that I have thrown into the trash for the day. I'm sure it isn't damaged too badly, it has only been placed in the trash a mere three hours ago. If I can sift through the other rubbage, I'm sure I can locate a loaf's worth." I say with all seriousness of tone and inflection.

"Excuse me?" David asks as if he didn't hear me.

"For your tea, I will have to secure a few tea bags as my morning shipment obviously is depleted and will not be replenished until early tomorrow. If I place enough used bags in a cup, I'm sure you will get the same flavor as using one new bag."

My words are sinking in as they are not certain if I'm serious or not. I can tell by the semi-confused glare as they stare back at me. The look is a mixture of appall, disbelief, and uncertainty. My expression to them however is confident, serious, and underlying humorous.

"I realize it is late in the evening and you probably have studies to tend to or other cares. I don't plan to keep you long. I can make sure I'm expedient in serving you. I can reduce my time of serving you by not washing dishes, yet serving you from cups that were recently used by other students. Since they were only used within minutes from your entrance, they probably are not as dirty as the set used this morning."

"Are you sassin' me boy?" David finally arrives at the notion that I'm making a fool of him and his friends.

"What do you mean? I'm trying my best to accommodate you."

His ignorance is personified by the silence that follows.

"Come on, let's leave. I don't want to eat here." he says as he turns to leave.

I watch David and his two friends walk out of my café and I don't think I will see them in here again. From the students I see in here from time to time, how many think like this yet never speak their true feelings? How many consider me lower class because I am a Negro student and not White? How many Negro students immediately bow down to the arrogance of the southern mentality of White people? How many lynchings have taken place just this year alone, a practice supposedly outlawed in this country? Fifty seven! How long will it take for those of the race to finally move up to their place and achieve some of the offerings of life laid out by DuBois and others? How long?

"Hello Henry!" Morgan says.

"Am I the first to arrive?" I ask.

"Oh no, Nate is her as is George Tompkins. Of course Robert is here as well."

"Splendid." I shake Morgan's hand heartily and enter the house. "Unusually timely we all are." I say to the entire room and not to a specific individual. Everyone response by laughing. George almost drops the wafer he is biting as he laughs and chews at the same time.

"We were testing one another to see how many of the society would be able to beat the punctual Henry Arthur Callis to the meeting." That invokes even more laughter. I've always counted myself a punctual individual for my appointments. I didn't realize it was so apparent to others. My father never tolerated lateness.

"Henry, I've been looking to speak to you." Robert says seriously.

"I wasn't aware."

"Can we spend a moment alone to..." as Robert seems to want to speak to me alone, C.C. walks into the house behind me. C.C. is the type of individual that commands attention when he enters any room and like any other meeting, draws attention as he enters this one.

"Gentlemen! Gentlemen! There is an autumn chill in the air indeed!" C.C. says smiling and patting his arms with his hands as the same time. For a man to always complain about the chilling temperatures, he is rarely seen in a coat heavier than his winter blazer. "I hope everyone is prepared to discuss as I have some literature that I would like to offer to the group for discussion."

"Prior to that discussion, if I may interrupt," Robert says, "I wish to submit to the group new information that I found."

"Oh most certainly." C.C. answers, "Please be our guest." C.C. takes off his blazer and scarf and takes a seat. I sit between George Tompkins and Nate and pay close attention to Robert who seems very serious-minded this evening. Robert is usually a straight face and serious individual, but something about this evening seems a bit different. He seemed excited and anxious to speak with me alone. Now he appears to be a bit more cautious than anxious. He seizes the moment nonetheless and prepares to make his presentation.

"Pardon me for the interruption my brothers but there is a bit of information that I wish to share with the entire group. I was out and I came across an extremely interesting bit of news from the Midwest region of the country."

George Kelley and Vertner enter the house. They take off their hats and quietly take open seats as it is very apparent that Robert has the floor. "What did I miss?" Vertner whispers to Morgan. Morgan leans toward him and whispers in his ear as Robert continues.

"There is an official Negro fraternity named Pi Gamma Omicron established at Ohio State University! They have journeyed along the same paths as we do right now! Yet they have gone forward and established a fraternal order for the men of their campus!" Robert states.

"How do you know this?" George Kelley asks.

"I read it in a newspaper article. It was in the Chicago Defender and I read it myself."

"This fraternal notion is not ideal! It will never work nor amount to much for a Negro student." George Tompkins has never been as vocal a he is at this moment. He has either abstained from voicing an opinion or silently given his allegiance to the literary idea more than the fraternal. This submittal by Robert has ignited a fervor in George in the cause of the literary society like never before. "The continuance of these debates is futile as we argue in circles with no clear end!"

"I don't think it is a weary idea, hence it continues to resurface." I add.

"Gentlemen, this discussion is pointless! A fraternity for Negro students is pointless and has no basis! I wish you few who insist on this notion would see these things from my perspective. I've been where you are. I've struggled through with my education as you all do. I have had ideas, visions, and too have worked hard to achieve what I've achieved thus far. For you who may not value my opinion as much," C.C. glances at George Kelley and rests his focus finally on me, "my opinion is not offered humbly, but boldly against the fraternal proposal. There is simply no basis."

Robert calmly interjects, "Sir, Ohio State University has proven your position incorrect. This Pi Gamma Omicron exists. We need to make full efforts to communicate with someone from the university to verify this claim."

"It is no more relevant if they exist than if they do not. That is not the issue here. The time you or any in this society waste in acquiring information on this claim could be well used toward the establishment of this literary society. We have needs and items to discuss. We have examinations to collect and archive. We have instructors and professors to speak with. This society needs to talk about furthering our efforts by acquiring new members. We should spend our time discussing facts of significance. The fact that over ten years ago, Charles Purvis so eloquently spoke out against lynching yet the barbaric practice still exists. Were any of you aware of his letter?" C.C. continues without allowing time for response. "Have any of you ever studied John Mercer Langston? Blanche Bruce?" Now he pauses. The answer is apparently no as surveyed by the silence in the room. "Yet you're quick to move forward with this idea that lacks foundation." C.C. catches himself in his own passionate delivery.

C.C. has undoubtedly shaken the good of us interested in the fraternal idea, if nothing else but with his desire to remain a literary organ. Nonetheless, Robert's claim has sparked a new life in those of us with the fraternal vision in our hearts. I definitely recognize the move of the spirit within my own being and the longing that has been placed there by my friends in similar clubs. As individuals, many of the men in this very room have expressed interest in the fraternal idea. Collectively, opinions vary more because of the influence of the literary society itself, or Mr. Poindexter, or the direction of the meetings or other obstacles. I believe that even C.C. will warm to the idea of fraternity and join the ranks if one were established. With his leadership style and capabilities, the organizing and efforts for such a task would be monumental. If the same passion he exhibits in rejecting the idea were funneled toward establishing the concept, only God knows what good we could do our fellow brother.

Φ

"Merry Christmas Robert!"

"Mr. Singleton, Christmas is three weeks past!" I say laughing while taking his hand. "I suppose it's more appropriate to say Happy New Year."

"Well then Happy New Year Robert!" Mr. Singleton is a simple man yet when he makes a statement, it leaves an impression. His smile is warm and receiving. His generosity seems to know no end. "How was your time spent back home?"

"I had a wonderful holiday break."

"The family is doing well?"

"Yes. All fine. I must admit that I missed it here."

"You missed Ithaca? I don't think I've ever heard any student, especially first year student, say anything like that."

"I have my reasons sir."

"Yes you do, and let me add..." Mr. Singleton leans toward me as if he is presenting me with secret information, "...she is quite beautiful!"

I laugh at the notion that Mr. Singleton knew my exact thoughts. I did miss Helen. We've built such a strong love for one another that each day away was worse and better than the day before. Worse because the days away compounded; better because the days left shortened. Either sense, we couldn't be together and were separated by more than mere distance. My thoughts floated to Helen constantly and continually.

"You're quite perceptive Mr. Singleton."

"Of course I am young Robert. Always remember, quiet individuals are watching and thinking. We occupy the capacity instead of speaking." he says quietly but confidently.

"Yes sir."

"Well I'm certain you have unpacking and things to tend to... oh I have a delivery for you. It's downstairs. Let me retrieve it for you."

"I can get it Mr. Singleton so you don't have to walk back up the stairs."

"No, no, I will get the package for you." Without another word, Mr. Singleton is out the door, down the hall, and down the stairs.

He's correct in his assumption that I do have unpacking to get to as well as things to get in order. I need to reach Henry, C.C., and the others. I don't know if everyone has returned to campus from the holidays yet. Most importantly, I need to see Helen. I want to see Helen. I miss Helen more today than I ever have. The fact that I'm close to her and have yet to communicate with her makes it worse. Deep down however, I know the reunion will transform bitter waters to sweet wine, all in due time.

"Robert here is your special delivery envelope. Signed, sealed, and delivered. I hope this doesn't mean that you will be leaving us." Mr. Singleton says as he hands me an envelope.

"Leaving you?" I question. I look at the envelope addressed to me, Mssr. R. H. Ogle, from Ohio State University in Columbus, Ohio. A response from Ohio State! "They responded to my letter! They've answered my letter!"

"What letter?"

I tear open at the envelope without answering Mr. Singleton's question because I'm so anxious to hear their response. I wrote to the university as soon as I heard of Pi Gamma Omicron. If what I read and believe is true, this will change the foundation of our society meetings. If indeed Negro students have come together to form a fraternity, we will have nothing else hindering us from movement in our own efforts. What bleak chance those of the society have of ever forming a fraternity could very well be enhanced by what has transpired in Ohio.

"It seems there are students, Negro students at Ohio University that have formed their own fraternity." I say as I drop the envelope and unfold the letter. "I wrote the university inquiring about their formation and existence. This is their..." Greetings Mssr. Ogle. I received your letter and hope to add clarity to the level of confusion that has been raised regarding a Pi Gamma Omicron group as one of our campus organizations. At this time, this office has no knowledge of any...

"What does it say?" Mr. Singleton asks.

It seems that I've been staring at this piece of paper for an eternity and have physically left the room that Mr. Singleton and I had been standing in. I left at least in my mind. As far as I'm concerned, the first word of the response letter took me out of the room and into the words of the page. The level of disappointment has yet to set in but my concentration on the letter instead of instant jubilation is a clear indication of the response.

"It... says..."

"You seem to be transfixed with your letter. I will let you get back to your unpacking."

Mr. Singleton's humbleness is overwhelming at times and instantly catapults me from the Ohio campus to the Ithaca campus and back where I'm standing. "Sir, I apologize. It's just that... well... the response letter is not what I'd hoped for." I fold the letter quickly and deposit it into my pocket. I pick the envelope off the floor. "I was wishing a different result."

Mr. Singleton smiles his warm smile. "Life disappoints at times Robert. The key to life is not that you do not encounter disappointments, but how you handle your encounters." With that, Mr. Singleton turns and is already in the hall. What a profound man.

Greetings Mssr. Ogle I received your letter and hope to add clarity to the level of confusion that... Greetings Mssr. Ogle, I received your letter and... life disappoints at times indeed. What's more disappointing than the response will be the reaction. I don't know what will be worse, the reaction from my friends who are clearly more in favor of the fraternal notion or my friends who are leaning toward literary. C.C. will beam with an unsaid satisfaction. He has been steadfast in his notion and unmovable. He stands strong for his position and makes it well known. Others of us have had differing thoughts on the two opposing ideologies. I've seen it. In some debates, a person will begin one way and the nature of the argument will sway him another way. He may enter the very next meeting swayed from the prior and be moved back to his original position. The votes would be deadlocked with C.C. casting the deciding and presiding. Essentially, he wins. Now with no ammunition, any symbolism of an opposition has withered.

Maybe I shouldn't tell C.C. and the others of the Ohio school response. If the group never becomes aware of the loss of ammunition on my part, they won't know of any upper hand that they may hold in this stalemate of sorts. I should speak to Henry and George about it though. I'm sure they are as anxious as I was to hear news of my inquiry. If I alert them, I will be telling all.

Nevertheless, I have things to unpack, classes to get prepared for, things to do, Helen to see. Helen and I made preparations beforehand to see one another right as I return. Nothing else consumed my thoughts as I traveled back to snowy Ithaca. The bitter cold temperatures I expected. The response from Ohio I didn't. I now must remove disappointing thoughts and focus on my objective; my lovely Helen.

"Good to see you Mr. Poindexter. How was your time away?"

"Work never ends Henry." C.C. says with a smile and a firm shake of my hand. "How was yours?"

"I had a wonderful holiday."

"Great. Good to hear of it. Now we're prepared to move forward steadily with a new semester?" C.C. states more than he asks.

"Yes sir." I respond. C.C. would make a great preacher. He speaks confidently and looks directly at you when he does. His confidence in speech and presentation is worthy of any pulpit and congregation. He seems to be the type of individual who can easily sway a man's opinion toward his own philosophy, much like many preachers that I know from my father's travels to various churches. He offers me a seat in his office.

"This is usually an interesting time of year here at Cornell."

"Why is that?" I ask.

"Many of the students who had such high aspirations just a few months ago either do not return or have a different focus because of situations that may be beyond their control." C.C. says.

"I see."

"In the position that I'm in, where I see so much, it gives me a feeling of hopelessness for the Negro students who cannot continue and matriculate. I realize how close they are. I see how in step they are with the rest of their lives, be that a positive step into a flourishing future. It rests though on sanctions made here on campus, in classrooms, and in books."

"I understand. How common of an occurrence is this?" I inquire.

"It happens. One time is far too many when education or ignorance are on the line." With that, C.C. is on to the next topic. "Henry, I want to discuss the current semester and the status of the literary society. I am very pleased with the group and the outcome of our meetings thus far. I am very pleased.

"I am as well."

"I must commend you on your efforts. You are a diligent thinker and have embraced your role as secretary with all sincerity."

"Thank you sir but there is really no need to shower me with accolades." I humbly reply.

"Oh but there is Henry. You've kept record of our transactions from the start and a very thorough scholar you have proven to be."

This makes me laugh because in my mind at least, I'm far less adequate and accurate and can always stand for a bit of improvement. "Thank you C.C., I'm certainly in no position to argue the point. I'll concede and be your scholar."

C.C. sits back in his chair and smiles, interlocking his

fingers in front of his face. He then stares at the ceiling as if in deep thought and careful choice of his next set of words. "Our goal now need be focused and straightway. We need to arrange programs on and off campus."

"Off campus?"

"Off campus. We have opportunity to not only educate the world within but also the world outside of the corners of Cornell."

"I am impressed by the fact that your focus and goal was to uplift the fellows being raised here at Cornell. Those who may have hardships and not share in the bond of... of friendship alone. I thought our mantle was to Cornell." I say.

C.C. smiles and stands up. He takes one step to his right, my left, and turns fully around to face his bookshelf. He then makes a quarter turn more to face me once again. "Henry, our mantle is education. Our mantle is the mantle passed down by our fathers. To raise a generation of men and women who will lead our race to a better place." He takes a book off of his shelf as if to show me something in it yet continues without opening the text. "You have to understand this calling Henry. We have been thrust into a state of being that requires due diligence. Due diligence to one another. We're on the verge of something extraordinaire". He takes his seat but leans forward across his desk toward me, eager and anxious. "We are on the crest of something paramount!" With that declaration, he stops. He places the book onto his desk but does not refer to it.

A peculiar quiet fills the air as do words. I don't know whether to respond or wait for his continuance. I wait.

"Henry," C.C. leans back in his chair and assumes his normal relaxed posture. "I guarantee the efforts of the society. I stand behind our purpose and I dedicate myself and the energies of all involved toward the less privileged. Be they matriculating at Cornell or not."

"I understand."

"Good. I knew you would." he says smiling. "We make a great partnership. I knew that upon meeting you and becoming acquainted. You have a lot of your father in you Henry and it's the leadership character that will always propel you, and propel our efforts.

"Thank you. That's kind of you to say but again, I'm no

leader. I'm just doing what I'm suppsed to do."

"Exactly!"

"I find it interesting that you requested my presence... actually rather surprising."

"Why?"

"I would think that based on the nature of our discussion, you would've spoken first to Robert, or C.C. or maybe Henry."

"Is there a difference?"

"Well... no, I guess."

"Then we're fine, Nothing further on that." Morgan is quick to close that door and reopen the former. "I have already stated that this conversation stays between you and I George."

"Of course. No need to further insure that." I reply.

"Thank you."

"Stop thanking me. You've thanked me several times already."

"Have I?" Morgan asks.

"You thanked me for meeting you on such short notice. You thanked me for agreeing to share with you in the sacredness of this discussion. You thanked me for my friendship and allegiance."

"Well I apologize for thanksgiving."

We both laugh.

Morgan isn't quite the joking type. Yet he isn't as serious as my namesake George Kelley either. It's actually difficult to determine what type of characteristic and personality trait best suits Morgan but I'm sure time will tell.

"I must say, you have tapped the conscious of my curiosity and haven't divulged the true meaning of our meeting. I'm eager to become fully aware."

"Now is the time." He becomes serious and quiet almost to a loud whisper. "Remember the night we met and I told of a certain professor that I felt treated me unfairly? With one of my assignments?"

"Oh yes, I do remember. I don't remember the name though."

"Dr. Platt."

"Right, right," I say. "I do recall now."

"I didn't fair so well in his class when final grades were returned." Morgan says.

"Really? Unjustly?"

Morgan takes a moment to contemplate my question. In this moment, I assume he is deciding how to answer. Either with a yes verdict in which an entire conspiracy theory would be launched propelling our entire group into the situation or a no verdict placing blame solely on Morgan and relieving Dr. Platt from any wrongdoing. Both answers involve the group and I know Morgan knows this. The yes answer initiates an investigation by the group as to the mistreatment of a Negro student by a formidable professor. With C.C. at the helm, this would be an unprecedented feat to assume, tackle and overcome. One I even recognize is a task we would wholeheartedly assume and not back down from. The no answer however brings the group in as a rallying force behind Morgan ensuring he has properly prepared for his classes and has all the requirements and criteria for matriculation. Both answers involve the society. Why would Morgan insist on only sharing with me and not informing the group of this predicament? Why not the group and why me?

"I can't place blame on the professor." he says. "I didn't bring last semester's meeting up to remind you of Dr. Platt. I brought it up to remind you of the class."

"I see." Actually, I don't see. A yes verdict would've made more sense to me in terms of not notifying the group. Maybe he feared a wide retaliation if scandal was brought to Dr. Platt's office. If there is no foul play on the part of the instructor, and the proper procedure is to make certain Morgan is best prepared for his studies, why not inform the group that can assist? "I must say then Morgan, I am quite perplexed as to the true nature of this conversation."

Morgan looks around the room before responding. He seems to try and stay aware of his surroundings at all times, constantly reminding himself of who is in our listening proximity. He doesn't appear nervous but extremely interested in who comes in and out of the library. Ironic that we would choose this as our meeting place if indeed Morgan has problems in his curriculum. "It would be natural for me to first approach Bob with this, him being my closest friend here at Cornell. At the same time, I recognize his position as a close friend and house mate..." Morgan pauses as if he wants to rethink the remaining fragment of his sentence. "... it's just that sometimes people are too close and with this I chose to notify him at a later date." He did rethink. "The reason I am letting you know is... well just to let you know. I needed to speak to someone."

"I'm glad you have notified me. Is there anything I can do?"

"No. I have a meeting with the department chair next week and I can let you know how that goes. It may require me retaking the class. I'll have to wait on their decision though, I'm sure."

"Sure. I understand. I'll be prepared to assist in any way possible once you notify me of your conclusions."

"Thank you."

"There you go thanking me again." I say with a smile.

I've never felt for anyone the way I feel for Helen. I've never felt for anyone half of what I feel for Helen and she assures me of the same. I don't know what is more reassuring; my feelings for her or confirmation of her feelings for me. Is there a stronger force of the two or does it matter? Nevertheless today is the appointed day. The day I've longed for since leaving Ithaca for Christmas. I see Helen today and I can barely contain my enthusiasm. Of course Mr. and Mrs.

Singleton are aware of my fancy and my excitement as this day approached. I've scarcely seen Morgan since his return. I believe he has been on campus verifying his schedule for the semester. Hence, I've contained all my emotion inside and I am ready to burst at the seams.

I had suggested our meeting take place at Charles' café. Helen insisted however a more neutral location and I agreed. The location wasn't quite as important as the meeting so whatever Helen suggests would be fine with me.

I've gone over in my mind dozens of times how this meeting will go. First salutations and then a hug. Deeper displays of affection will obviously be limited pending our location. I'm sure we will talk and catch one another up on our holidays, gift giving, lavish dinners and the like. Christmas in Ithaca must be a snowy treat. I have a handkerchief that I personally gift wrapped that I know she will love. That gift is actually on the suggestion of my mother. I don't know if she even thought about getting me a Christmas gift. Seeing her and having her close is gift enough for me. I hope she realizes that.

I arrive early at our lovely wooded meeting place. Helen and I have chosen to walk these paths a few times last semester. These trees have been privy to some of the deepest conversations an in love couple can have. I've been the fortunate one in that those conversations originated from my very soul and flowed from my lips and not someone else's to Helen. I know that showing up more than punctual only shows my eagerness but my feelings on display haven't been an issue with Helen.

I remember our first conversation here. I first told Helen about George Kelley and Henry and about C.C. and Vertner and the others. I told her about the literary society and how we had plans to develop and institute our own fraternity. The likes of which have not been seen at Cornell. She listened intuitively as I told her my ideas for a fraternity of brothers who would be accountable to one another. I told her how George Kelley ignited us all with his passion to research this fraternal notion and how some in the group opposed. Helen became familiar with all of the members of the group, especially Morgan obviously. Helen never gave the impression that our task at our fraternity would be impossible or improbable.

Most who have heard of our aspirations quickly denounce the idea and alert us to how foolhardy the notion is yet some embrace our vision and grab hold to it, whether involved or not. Helen, clearly not involved, has chosen to support me and our vision whether she fully understands it or not.

As Helen approaches I gaze upon her beauty as never before. Her face is glowing and shining more than the snow around us. Without even a hello or any other words we embrace. Helen in my arms is my best revelation of heaven. I close my eyes and cherish this moment; the moment I've dreamt of and thought about for weeks. I rub her back and hold her close to me and the only words that I can think of, the only words that my soul will allow me to utter come forth as nothing more than a whisper. "I've missed you."

Helen doesn't verbally respond but as we let go of one another, her tears are enough of a response for me. She looks down and away from me as to shield the fact that she is crying. I take her by the chin and raise her head to look deep into her eyes. "Helen, it does my heart good to see you. I've thought of nothing else during my time away then to hold you once again."

"Oh Robert..." she murmurs.

"We mustn't take such long vacations." I say smiling.

"I have something to tell you." she says staring back at me.

Although I know she is overjoyed to see me as I am to see her, her face has an appearance of sadness which instantly concerns me. Her sadness is not necessarily confirmed because of her tears, but through her tone and reservation.

"What is it my love? Is everything alright?" I ask growing concerned.

With her next statement a new stream of tears fall reminiscent of the very waterfall backdrop of our walking trail today.

"I'm pregnant."

Time stops. Water stops streaming. Snow stops crunching beneath my feet. Tears continue to fall.

"You're... you're... pregnant?"

"Yes."

She comes toward me and hugs me with a much tighter embrace than initially. Now her streaming tears become a full cry. I hear her, I feel her, I hold her.

"Well... are you sure?" I ask.

I realize instantly the frailty of this question. She lets me go and steps back once again. She needs to see my response.

"Yes... um... I'm positive."

At this moment, I realize all that Helen really means to me; much more than I thought before. This moment in time transfixes us and bonds us as family. I must reassure her and love her, now more than ever before.

"Helen, I love you and this is wonderful news for us. I will do all that I have to do by you and with you. Rest assured of that. I love you more than life and I always will."

Helen's tears transform from streaming tears of fear, doubt, uncertainty, and possibly regret to love, warmth and security. Our embrace now is what it was supposed to be at first; a loving embrace signifying the passion that exists between us. Her news has surprised me and will settle in later I'm sure. I'm certain to feel the uncertainty and fear behind this. For now, holding Helen Moore and an unborn child is all that occupies my mind and heart. This is the greatest Christmas present Helen could've ever given me.

C.C. opens the meeting with a holiday greeting. "I trust that everyone had a wonderful holiday break and is as eager and anxious for what this year of nineteen hundred and six holds for all of us as a group. I see we have a new student in our midst. Would you like to introduce yourself sir?"

"Certainly." The medium height, dark complexion gentleman stands and announces himself." My name is James Morton and I have been made aware of the meetings of this literary group. I became immediately interested and want to lend my participation." James takes his seat.

Mr. Newton chimes in, "It's good to see you sir and

everyone else who is well sna accounted for."

Mr. Newton chimes in.

"Thank you sir." I say. "It's good to see you as well." He nods in my direction.

"Since you spoke up first Nathaniel," C.C. says, "why don't you be the first to tell us about your holiday and your expectations for this year."

"In the hot seat you are huh Nate?" Vertner blurts out. Everyone either smiles or chuckles after Vertner's outburst.

"I had a good time with my family. I didn't think of any of you guys once." My sarcasm indicated clearly that I was merely joking and everyone in the group seemed to understand by laughing. "I expect great things from this group this year. I see us reaching more people and possibly adding numbers to this group such as Mr. Morton. I also see us resting on a permanent foundation of what we are to be." I leave it at that. Henry is next. I look to Henry on my right instead of C.C. who is seated to my left.

"My father, brother and I had a quiet Christmas. I did some reading and became more familiar with some of the work of W.E.B. DuBois. Some of his documents are quite interesting. I will have to share with the group very soon."

"Please do! It's good to hear that Henry." C.C. says like a proud father.

"This group," Henry continues, "has the potential to expand and broaden the minds of Negro students who are separated by unfamiliarity. Merely looking around this room, we were students who had no knowledge of one another. The call brought forth enables us to assemble and know one another and call each other brother. With that established, we have the ability to further that directive and extend ourselves to others in like circumstances as we. I hope we accomplish that this year."

"Well put Henry." C.C. concludes. "I know everyone agrees."

"My father had the audacity to put me to work!" Everyone laughs including Vertner who makes claim to the statement. "He was working on designs for a local establishment. I served a few weeks as his apprentice. It wasn't so bad, I did learn a few things working so close. I had never known some of the fundamental things of the practice. So that concludes on my working holiday. When I ponder what this year holds for me or holds for us, I believe it rests on the shoulders of us all and is up to all to capitalize as much as possible. We must work hard and then work harder. We have to think creatively then rethink what we come up with. If this is going to be a fraternity endeavor, then let us move in that direction without fear or unwillingness but boldness and sureness of decision." Vertner is first to mention fraternity. He continues and doesn't allow time to rebut. "Whatever decision we make, let it be made for the betterment of ourselves, our fellow students, and students to come. If we argue, then damn let it be a fight to the finish. Then get up, clean ourselves, and fight again." He closes with a smile and returns to Vertner as usual.

The following moment of silence indicates everyone's position. They were either taken aback at his mention of fraternity or his serious tone in closing which we had not been accustomed to from Vertner. More than likely the former, I included. Nonetheless, George Tompkins is next and he breaks the silence carefully.

"This literary society is a serious brainchild and powerful vehicle in the movement of the Negro mind from closed to open." George being the first to state literary society. "Even in Henry's mentioning of DuBois and his excerpts, we should investigate those and research his philosophy. We must look to a variety of authors and subjects. We must educate one another and then educate those on the outside of the literary society," George mentions again, this time sounding more purposeful, "so they too can learn from our growing and vast pool of knowledge. Have any of you become familiar with author and critic William Ferris?" Before any of us have a chance to respond, not that I believe any would, George pulls a small piece of paper out of his pocket and reads. "'He grovels in the mud and mire of Southern prejudice to gratify an itching palm and please the White man in the South.' William is referring to Booker T. Washington and his ideologies and I agree with his assessment wholeheartedly. These are the kinds of subjects we need to discuss." George nods to indicate his conclusion not realizing he never mentioned his Christmas holiday. I'm surprised he carries quotes from writers in his pockets.

"My holiday was quiet like Henry's," states Charles. It's good to be back and good to see you all. I look forward to sharp discussions and hard work to achieve our endeavors."

"I had a pleasant time away," George B. states. It is definitely time to turn our thoughts to the efforts of decision making and foundation lying. The task before us is within our grasp and very much achievable. We need not rest until our goals are obtained and..."

"What goals and tasks are you referring to George?" C.C. quickly interjects his question before George can finish.

"The idea that continues to resonate in many of our spirits, the fraternal idea," George states with confidence.

George's response quiets C.C. and lends another moment of silence to the room. Robert, who is seated next to George, doesn't know if he should tell us of his holiday or wait for George to continue.

"I uh... I had a nice Christmas and... it's good to be back. Happy New Year everyone," Robert's glance never leaves the floor and his statement sounds as unsure as his posture. If any a time in this informal gathering a time of awkwardness, now is it. The normally sure Robert seems at a loss for space, time and words.

"Happy New Year to you too Bob," Vertner breaks the tense moment.

"George,"" C.C. chimes in immediately, "do you honestly feel the fraternal idea even exists within our hearts?" Before George B. has moment to answer, "We've each had time to defuse the notion by being apart and reflecting on the true issue at hand."

"True issue?" George responds.

"Truest of issues. Each of you had grades to collect, scores to tally and classes to register in as this new semester approached. It is a relief to me personally to see everyone accounted for as there have been many Januaries that this has not been the case. That is why literary is the obvious and clear option. Your academic success has been on even your mind, on Henry's mind, on my mind on Nathaniel's mind." C.C. puts his hand on my shoulder as he stands.

"All true indeed. Notwithstanding sir the relevance and necessity of an aspect of brotherhood and secrecy," George replies confidently.

"Preposterous and foolhardy!" C.C. explodes.

"Sirs." Mr. Newton speaks up, very uncommon within our meetings. "What is foolhardy is to bicker and frustrate each other during these proceedings."

"I apologize gentlemen if I began to frustrate the group," George B. concedes.

"No, no, I need to apologize," C.C., always the diplomat. "No need for outbursts of any kind." Referring to himself. Chastising himself... to a small extent at least. "Let's hear from Morgan."

Everyone's attention turns toward Morgan who has patiently waited his turn. "It's good to see everyone and I too look forward to what this year will bring. What's ahead? Looks like we have plenty to discuss and decide."

Morgan's brief remarks initiate C.C. to continue with the meeting. "Once again, it's good to have everyone back. I shared with the group the students I have met in my time here at Cornell and the disappointment I felt upon them not returning. It's good to know that at least academically, you are all sound."

If nothing else, Mr. Poindexter is genuinely concerned with our welfare. His position seems to be one of a strong supporter of our academic standing, much more than our social aspirations as this group. I've personally felt comfortable with C.C. especially in a position of leadership within this group. I'm sure if any in the group had problems in their academics, they would feel as comfortable as I do approaching C.C. and resolving the matter expeditiously.

"You wanted to see me... or I suppose us?" I ask C.C. as he comes into his own office late for a meeting with me and George Tompkins. I can't say that I am not irritated by the fact that I've been waiting fifteen minutes for a meeting that I was not aware of until today.

"I apologize for my tardiness gentlemen. I trust you have made yourselves comfortable in my humble place." C.C. says as he hangs his hat and scarf on the back of the door.

"We have been quite entertained with each other's conversation," George says, "I didn't know Charles was such a fellow, such a well-versed business man."

I change my glance from C.C. who has evoked irritation to George Tompkins who has evoked surprise. We have been sitting here quietly, waiting for this mysterious meeting to begin. I don't know any more or less about George Tompkins then what I learned in the various meetings that the society has had over the course of this semester and last. Has he learned something about my business practices somehow through the dead silence that has surrounded us over the past fifteen minutes? If so, I would hope he would share this trick with the rest of the society so we can all attempt to try it with some of the professors on campus.

"Good. I have heard of our café Charles and I must say that is quite impressive. Quite impressive indeed. Tell me. What brings an older student like yourself to the hallowed grounds of Cornell? Why at this stage of your life did you wish to pursue a higher education?" C.C. asks as he sits behind his desk.

"One can never stop achieving or learning. I'm sure you advocate that. Tragedy is not to not accomplish. Tragedy is to accomplish and then grow complacent, then to cease growing."

"That is an interesting philosophy. Who are you quoting?" George turns and asks.

"Myself. Didn't you just hear me say it?" There is a brief silence. I smile and invite both C.C. and George to laugh. My demeanor is usually stern and curious. Although I enjoy a good laugh at times, I usually have many diverse thoughts that consume me and present me as a thinker. My colleagues don't know when to laugh with me, as indicated just now with George and C.C. I would consider myself the opposite of a Vertner Tandy.

"That's a good one Charles. I like your wit." C.C. chimes in as he chuckles.

My wit?

"I've called the two of you here for a specific reason." C.C. begins this new sentiment with a much more serious tone. "As you know, the society is benefiting well from the ongoing contributions of its members and its leadership. I couldn't be happier with the results thus far and the outlook for where this literary organ could take us."

"I agree." George says wholeheartedly. George's outburst would've interrupted me had I been speaking but C.C. continues undaunted.

"I recognize the clear path and direction that we need to focus on and travel down. It is neither mystery nor surprise to you that my feelings toward this group are strong and my will is equally as strong. I don't tire nor back down easily." C.C. speaks boldly and confidently.

I however still question my attendance in this impromptu meeting while my younger colleague George Tompkins seems to be quite enthralled with Mr. Poindexter.

"I'm not quite sure I understand the relevance, or should I say my relevance in this meeting." I blurt out. I don't necessarily need to know that C.C. is strong about his convictions with the literary society. I see that every time we vote. I witness that every time we debate. I hear it every time we gather together. "To be quite frank Mr. Poindexter, I do have a few items to tend to."

C.C. smiles and brings his hands together almost at the speed of a clap. "That is the exact reason you were summoned here Charles! Exactly! You are a business man. You are serious about what it is that you do. I respect that. I respect that greatly. You are a man about your convictions and we could all learn from a gentleman such as yourself. I know that in our votes for literary society or fraternal, your vote has leaned on the side of the literary society. On the more serious side. The side with foundation and merit. The sound side. I want to let you know that our efforts at keeping our organization true to its ideals and purpose will not die nor will we waiver in our attempts. In any of our attempts."

"That's good to hear and know C.C." George says. "I for one walk on the path of progress. I understand the vision and the responsibility we have to one another and to those coming after us."

"Outstanding." C.C. shifts in his seat before continuing. "The reason for this impromptu gathering is this... we need to increase our efforts and further our resolve. We cannot allow some of the ideas that are being brought forth to fester and mature and come to pass. Understand this gentlemen." C.C. stands up and walks to the side of his desk. "I understand the mentality of others in the group. It may not seem as if I do, but I do. I don't agree or acquiesce, but I understand. I've been where these young men are. I have experienced the college days and have learned a great deal from them. Hence, I know what is best for this group. What is best for this group is not some path that has been laid by our White counterparts. What is best for this group is what is undeniably the prerequisite to success. Education. We have to excel and help others do the same. That is the hallmark and that is the bottom line. I called you here George and I called you here Charles to ensure we are embarking on the same vision. Those of us who are undeniably and steadfast on the course of what is right and what is necessary need to bond and work in unison to see the society be what it can and shall be.

"I appreciate your resolve and your unwavering attitude toward what we are attempting to build. I have always been impressed with your confident delivery and your stance. You don't have to convince me of your motives or what you feel is the good of all concerned." I remind C.C.

"Good. Then I count you in as one among us who champions our cause for the good of the group and for the good of the vote."

I now understand why C.C. summoned me to his office. He wants to secure as many solid votes as he can toward the literary component in opposition to the fraternal notion. As long as opinions do not sway, he casts the deciding vote favoring the literary. He cannot afford for a shift in the thinking of anyone who is on his side or the vote would switch. He probably feels that George is a secure vote. I would agree. He called me here today possibly because he feels the same about me. I am not as wholeheartedly for literary as much as he thinks otherwise. Personally, what is good for the group is what I will vote for. The fraternal notion, albeit not a bad notion, hasn't sustained for me enough evidence of its relevance or necessity. Not saying that it can't and not saying that it won't. It hasn't as of yet.

"I hate to interrupt your reading but I need to talk to you." Morgan says as he enters my room.

"It's quite alright." I turn and say. I clear my throat.

"Robert, are you feeling well? What is the problem?"

I didn't mean for Morgan or anyone for that matter to see me like this. I don't normally lock my door. Not when I am in my room at least. Morgan and I have always maintained a friendship where we enter each other's room as often and as care free as we want. If anything, it more likely would've caused immediate suspicion and alarm if I had locked my door while sitting inside my room.

"I'm fine."

"I know you a bit better than that I would hope. You aren't the one to find crying or upset like this. Is everything well back home? Do you have news from the family?" He asks with growing concern.

"Morgan I don't mean to alarm you and I apologize. It's just that... well, right now I have a lot on my mind. I have decisions to make and..." I really cannot find the words to express myself. This is unlike me.

"Robert this is not like you. You have to tell me what is happening. Did you get a bad report from your instructors? Are you not doing well in classes? Is it Helen? What has you in such a state?" Morgan strikes the issue head on but doesn't realize it. The silence between us only serves to intensify an already tense environment as neither of us knows the next proper thing to say. He not knowing what to say in order for me to reveal and me not knowing how quite to explain my predicament for lack of a better term.

"Morgan, you are my best friend."

"Indeed." He replies.

"What I am to share with you has to remain as private as anything you have ever held close in your life. Can you promise me that?"

"Most certainly. With all assuredness. Now what is the problem?"

I take a deep breath and rub both hands across my face before I begin. "Helen and I are considering getting married."

"What! Getting married? Are you out of your mind?"

"Keep your voice down! I don't want Mr. and Mrs. Singleton to be made aware. Not yet."

Morgan looks around as if they are hiding in the room with us. He then lowers both his voice and his head as he leans toward me.

"What would make you dream up such a notion? You want to get married? Here? Now? Have you gone mad?"

"No I haven't gone mad. I love Helen with all my heart." I say sincerely.

"I know you do but marriage? You want to get married? Even if you pursue, her parents are never going to agree."

"They are going to have to. We're having a baby."

Morgan is speechless as I would expect. I don't know who is more surprised; Morgan for hearing it or me for saying it. At some point, I am going to have to tell everyone. My family, Helen's parents and family, my colleagues at Cornell, Mr. and Mrs. Singleton, and of course my brothers in the society. Morgan being the first was a huge hurdle to get over. It also is amazing how it sounds. We're having a baby. To this point, my conversations with Helen, with myself, and with God have been, Helen is pregnant. We're having a baby sounds and feels different. It feels like the family I keep insisting to Helen that we can and will create. It is reassuring. It is confirming. It is restoring. "Helen and I are having a baby."

"Oh my. Um..." Morgan laughs and runs his fingers through his hair. His hand rests on the back of his neck and he changes in his chair uncomfortably. "You got Helen... you're going to have a baby?"

"Yes. I'm going to have a baby." Another round of silence as this news begins to settle in and take hold of the mind.

"I have to marry her."

"Oh you're right. You're absolutely right. You can't argue with that. You have to get married. Do you really love her?"

"I love Helen more than life itself. She is my every day joy and the reason I love to wake up in the morning. When she told me of this great news, I wasn't scared. I wasn't happy either. I just... I just was. I know that is hard to understand without being there."

"I may not understand that particular instance. No, I wasn't there. I do however, see the change in you. I have known you for a long time and you being with Helen is clear. You are in love and that cannot be denied. It's in your smile. It's in everything you seem to do lately. She consumes you. I think it is wonderful and I wish you well in informing the Moores."

"Yes, I have thought about that. It's strange to me because at one moment I am the happiest man alive. I love her. I love her deeply Morgan. Yet I am scared of raising a child. I'm in college. Helen hasn't graduated high school yet. Although she loves me dearly and I can both see and feel her passion for me..." Silence. This is the reason Morgan caught me in an emotional state. All I have to do is say it and all the emotion comes right back. It doesn't matter how hard I try. It doesn't matter how long I practice holding back. If tears decide to fall, they will overwhelm your will and fall. I didn't want to ruin Helen's life by taking her out of the joys of high school. I didn't want to embarrass her in front of her friends or peers. Helen comes from the Moore house. She is well known and respected in Ithaca. This is not something she would... we have to get married. We have to. "I am a little at a loss for words Morgan and I apologize. Not like me to be at a loss for anything."

"I understand. If you want, I can... you know, come back at a better time." Morgan stands as if to leave.

"There is no better time."

"I suppose you're right. I guess I can't come back when she's not pregnant anymore." Morgan says as he smiles and sits back down. His statement causes me a much needed laugh.

"No, I guess you can't."

"So when are you thinking about having a wedding?" He asks.

"March. Helen and I spoke about it. So we are thinking March."

"That is right away. How will you manage?

"I will manage for the love of Helen." Either my statement or the thought of a wedding in a few short weeks has silenced the two of us again. Morgan and I have not been this silence in conversation with one another since we met. To hear me, Bob Ogle, talk about Helen the way that I do I guess can be overwhelming to many of my friends.

"The thought is quite shocking. Married. A father." Silence grips him again until he decides to break it. "Have you informed anyone else as of yet?"

"No, you are the privileged first to know," I say confidently with a smile.

"Well it is safe with me until such a time as you want to let others know."

"Thank you. I appreciate your respect. I don't have much time in informing. As you stated, March is upon us."

"Yes it is. How is Helen taking everything?"

"She is taking it well, much better than I would've expected actually. The main force behind her peace is her love. Helen loves me as much as I love her. That is our road map and our guide and we have decided that no matter what happens, that will direct us." Morgan leans back and smiles. "Who would've thought that you would meet the love of your life that night? I certainly never would've imagined that."

"Me neither. Trust me, me neither."

We both refuse to let this silence overtake us as we both begin to speak at the same time. "I'm sorry, you go ahead." He says.

"No, what were you going to say?" I respond.

"Well, I just wanted to thank you for letting me know first. I know it must be both joyous and difficult but know that I am a friend. I always have been and I always will be a friend." Morgan extends his hand to me. I take it firmly and look him directly into his eyes.

"Thank you. That means a lot to me."

"No problem." Morgan gets up and moves toward the door to leave.

"Oh wait, what was it you wanted to tell me when you came in?"

He stops an turns back toward me. "Oh nothing. Never you mind that. You have much more important things to ponder. We can discuss that some other time."

Sigma Alpha Epsilon was founded on March 9, 1856 at the University of Alabama at Tuscaloosa. They maintain an impressive coat of arms and sport attractive colors. Within their history lies the inner makings of a great story of perseverance as they were able to survive one of the most tumultuous times this country has ever known. The fraternity almost ceased to exist during the Civil War as most of its members were chosen for the Confederacy. Yet the dream and vision did not die but instead remained in the hearts of an earnest few. These select few were able to resurrect the purpose and forge ahead to the many chapters that exist today.

One of the campus events, the most talked about event on the Sigma Alpha Epsilon calendar is the Valentine's Night Banquet. Held at an off campus hall, this event is extravagant in every syllable of the word. The brothers of the fraternity do their best to out-court one another with their evening guest.

Everyone is preparing to wear their best, eat the finest, and hear a rousing speech from one or more of their members.

As I enter the hall, I'm greeted by Mortimer who is also working the evening. Unlike myself, I believe he is interested in membership in Sigma Alpha Epsilon, hence his willingness to wait tables this evening.

"Good evening Henry." Mortimer states as he extends his hand to me.

"Mortimer, you're here early." I take his hand and match his warm smile.

"I didn't want to miss anything. I've heard that this is a fantastic event. I would like to see for myself."

"Good for you. I have heard it is well beyond its accolades." I say.

"It's a bit cold this evening. I hope that won't deter attendance." He says.

"Oh no. I know that many of the brothers and their guests have been looking forward to this for weeks. A little chill in the air won't keep them away."

"What of yourself? Shouldn't you be off tickling your fancy with a nice guest on this your first Valentine's Day in Ithaca?"

I smile, almost bashfully, albeit having no reason to be bashful. "Duty first." I reply.

As the guests begin to arrive, it is almost a magical evening of elegance. I have never seen the members of the fraternity dressed in their best as I do tonight. Brothers are cordial to one another and to their guests. Nicholas McGarner, the president of the chapter arrives with his girlfriend Mary. They are as well-known as a couple as he is as an athlete on campus. He is well respected, well liked, and noted to go far in life. Sig Alpha brothers are both pleased and lucky to have a leader like Nicholas in that he is diligent in his efforts, whatever his efforts are.

I consider it my good fortune to be in the company of such an event. I am a firsthand witness, not being a member of the fraternity, to their goings on and their productions. It is interesting to me that a member of another fraternity would not be allowed into the reception room or dining hall tonight yet I, as a waiter and clearly not a member of Sigma Alpha

Epsilon, am allowed to watch the proceedings. Maybe because of my fellowship with the members throughout my time in the house last semester. Or possibly the friendships I have gained from the members who are cordial and forthcoming with valuable information toward the forming of our own organization. Maybe because it's my job. Nevertheless, I plan to observe and witness firsthand some of the key ingredients in the making and creating of a fraternal banquet. Nicholas, also serving as the evening's toastmaster, gathers the brothers and their guests and invites them into the dining hall for dinner. The ladies are seated and before the gents take their seats, they join in singing the Alma Mater, a feat I have never witnessed of the fraternity members before.

Nicholas then begins with opening remarks. "Members of Sigma Alpha Epsilon and our guests, I Nicholas McGarner formally welcome you to our Valentine's Banquet 1906. Please enjoy yourselves, take pleasure in the meal and feel free to exchange tall tales of dragons slain and fair maidens rescued." Everyone laughs at Nicholas' charm. "Let us eat until we can eat no more!"

The meal, a fabulous course, consists of stuffed fat geese broiled Lombard style and covered with sliced almonds, Turkish style rice with milk sprinkled with cinnamon, cabbage soup with sausages, prosciutto cooked in wine serve with capers and grape pulp, Parmesan and Riviera cheese, rolled bread, pear tarts wrapped in marzipan, ring shaped cakes, wafers and Sigma Alpha Epsilon punch.

I smile, shake hands, respond to cordial and formal introductions, and serve the brothers in attendance. Mortimer does much of the same, yet not nearly on the assignment that I am. My own personal quest is to listen and learn; much of what I have done over the course of the fall, much that has been useful in the formulation of my thoughts and ideas.

At the conclusion of dinner, much chatter, and much laughter, Nicholas, who has a way of quieting a room, takes the floor by addressing the audience once again. "Members of Sigma Alpha Epsilon and invited guests, welcome. The true gentleman is the man whose conduct proceeds from good will and an acute sense of propriety, and whose self-control is equal to all emergencies; who does not make the poor man conscious of his poverty, the obscure man of his obscurity, or any man of his inferiority or deformity; who is himself humbled if necessity compels him to humble another; who does not flatter wealth, cringe before power, or boast of his own possessions or achievements; who speaks with frankness but always with sincerity and sympathy; whose deed follows his word; who thinks of the rights and feelings of others, rather than his own; and who appears well in any company, a man with whom honor is sacred and virtue is safe. These words are familiar to us all yet move us with purpose and place us on course for fulfillment. These cannot be deemed words to a speech. Rather a call to life and virtue. I implore each of you to listen to the sentiment behind this great declaration and choose it as your own. When you are far removed yet never fully from the grounds of Cornell, remember Sig Alpha as home. Sig Alpha will remember you. Do for your fellow man as Sigma Alpha has done for you. Achieve past your dreams as Sigma Alpha has instructed you to. Remember the legacy that Sigma Alpha Epsilon has built and realize that you are a growing part. We all, by cultivation of all that is pure in a man's nature and character will achieve the ideals of his fraternity."

The remainder of the evening is followed by brother after brother giving speech after speech. None however as moving nor as eloquent as the one given by Nicholas. His words, although some of which have some secrecy that only brothers of the order would know, resounded in my very spirit. What if George Biddle Kelley were addressing the society and gave a resounding speech? What if Vertner Tandy were the toastmaster? What if Robert Harold Ogle gave the keynote? What if I spoke on a fraternity's purpose? What if C.C. gave a speech on the need for a literary component in a fraternal body?

The Sage College opened its door over thirty years ago. I have never seen a facility which compares with it either here or in West Virginia. The furniture is authentic oak and mahogany. The tapestry is fine linen with accessories to match. Philanthropists in their contributions to Cornell have constructed this hall to be what would be a premier dormitory on almost any campus. Students are preferred if they have residence in Sage. The dining facility in which I work is set to host banquets, dinners or special services. I began my employment experience at Sage last year and have worked diligently, moving up to position of headwaiter. My position is esteemed; especially among Negroes here at Cornell. Some would never consider a Colored person with a staff of White students.

On this crisp afternoon, I've agreed to sit and converse with Charles Chapman. I believe we are equally impressed with one another. He with me and my established rank here at Sage Room and me with he and his business intuitiveness. I not only have cleared my afternoon for our meeting, but have cleared a sitting area in the dining room where we can be served coffee, cheese and crackers.

"Hello James, good to see you again." Charles says approaching. He removes his hat and top coat as I offer him his seat.

"Good to see you again as well. Glad you had some time that we could sit and talk."

"I made time. I reived your message and wanted to talk right away. I didn't know that you were employed here." Charles takes a look around the place as he crosses his legs and leans back. "This is a beautiful room."

"We try our best to maintain it. It isn't very old."

"Looks well kept. What exactly is your role here?"

"I am the headwaiter. Mentioning, can I get you something? Coffee? Cheese and crackers?"

"Please." Charles says.

"Sure, please excuse me." I stand not to retrieve his coffee, but to give instruction to Dickson to gather the items for Charles and myself. I sit back down. "I wanted to talk to you today about the literary society. I think the notion is extremely interesting and found it quite intriguing when I first heard of the effort."

"How did you hear?" Charles asks.

"I overheard Nathaniel speaking of it as I was leaving work one day. I decided to ask him and he directed me to the

#tdlchapter

home of Mr. Newton."

"Very good. I see we have an easy task at growing our group with simple invitations of good men like yourself."

I smile at Charles' compliment. "Thank you sir. My question however, is to the purpose of the group. I was made privy to the meeting discussion and the... well, the debate that ensued. The entire process interested me as I witnessed the gentleman speak on his desire at fraternity."

"You must be speaking of George Kelley."

"Yes, I believe that was his name. His position was very interesting. I see the fraternities here in the dining room all the time. I see them plan and implement their banquets and events right here."

"Really? What are those affairs like?" Charles looks up above where I am seated across from him, indicating Dickson has arrived with the pastries and coffee I ordered.

"Thank you." I say as Dickson places the items before Charles and me. We resume speaking once he leaves.

"The fraternity events are wonderful. They spare no expense and the food and decorations are exquisite."

"That is interesting." Charles seems to go into deep thought as he partakes in the cheese.

"I would never consider Colored students participating in anything of that nature, until I arrived at the Newton home. After the society meeting, I have thought of nothing else."

"You seem to be a hard worker James and diligent about your business. I think the society would be greatly appreciative of any efforts you offer, be they ideas or labor."

"Thank you. I am willing to contribute toward any efforts." I offer.

If ever I could hear or feel excitement leap from the pages of a piece of paper, it was when I read the brief note left for me by Henry. In simply the need to meet, Henry has a way of heightening one's level of expectancy. Especially since he and I share in the commonality of our one true purpose. I am anxious for him to arrive at this our meeting place. Henry and I have met here at the edge of the formal campus several times. A few times with Nathaniel. Once with Vertner and once with Charles Chapman. Some of the most noteworthy conversations I have had have been between Henry and I in this very location. I perceive this to be similar.

Henry and I met here when he fully described for me the social function of the Sigma Alpha Epsilon fraternity a few weeks ago. Henry was thoroughly impressed with everything about their evening; from the placements to the menu to the conduct and attitude toward the affair. A new fire was ignited in Henry that will be difficult to quench. Since Henry and I are of one mind on several subjects, it is fair reason to believe I will also be a hard one to settle once we overcome some of the obstacles set before us.

"George!" I turn around to see Nathaniel approaching me. I suppose this will not be only Henry and I.

"Brother Nathaniel. It's good to see you. I suppose you received a note from Brother Henry as well."

"Indeed. Henry knows how to pluck at the levels of curiosity." Nathaniel says as he laughs.

"It is one of the fond attributes to our friend Henry. His diligence and ability to raise curiosity levels." We both laugh.

"What do you think this conversation is about?"

"I don't know." I reply. "Did he tell you about the Valentine's banquet that he attended as a waiter?"

"No, he didn't. Was it a well-attended event?"

"I do know that Henry is quite satisfied that he attended. He was able to witness first hand a lot of the inner scenes of their social gathering. He was extremely impressed and overwhelmed."

"Is that so? I will have to ask him for myself." Nathaniel says. Nathaniel is a factual person with a tremendous spirit and great personality. He smiles often without speaking and shares in a good laugh with the other fellows. Yet he is a very serious student about his business and is more than on the side of fraternity in our efforts. When Henry summons me to a side bar meeting such as this and Nathaniel arrives, I know that great conversations are to be had because we discuss the success of our platforms. To create and own a fraternity for ourselves gaining momentum and support from Colored students, faculty and community residents of Ithaca.

"Punctual as always fellows!" Henry says approaching. Henry's smile is warm and inviting.

"You always grab my attention," Nathaniel says. "I make it a point to be on time as to not miss a single item."

"It is well appreciated."

"So what is this business about?" I ask growing curious as I realize that the time has now come that this very question will be answered.

"Let's have a seat." Henry offers.

We choose a nearby bench and sit down. All attention remains on Henry.

"I don't know if I was in my right to do this but if anyone could advise on the topic, it was definitely Nathaniel and George Kelley." Henry says. "That is the purpose for my note. I took it upon myself to research a name and although I have not properly revealed its definitive meaning even to myself, I want to receive your response. Our society needs a name, an identifiable and qualitative mark for the campus. Not just the society but a name, a real name.

Henry is absolutely right. "How did you come up with a name? What is it?" I ask.

Professor Hiram Corson is a well-liked and well noted instructor and is head of the English Language and Literature Department. Dr. Charles Edwin Bennett is the Professor of Latin and Professor George Prentice Bristol is the Professor of Greek Studies. The three happened to be in the company of one another as I enter the office, primarily to visit Professor Bristol.

"Sir, my name is Henry Callis and I have set an appointment with Professor Bristol."

"Yes Henry, I will gather him for you." Professor Corson

states. Professor Corson is one of the highest respected faculty members at Cornell. Although I have never met him personally before today, I immediately know who he is by the manner in which he carries himself. He walks into a back area; an area that could be used as another office but it more so used for storage. When Professor Corsen returns, he has with him Professor Briston and Professor Bennett.

"George, this is Henry... Callis is it?" Professor Cosron asks.

"Yes sir. Henry Callis."

"Right. Henry Callis. This is Professor Bristol and this is Professor Bennett.

Professor Bristol extends his hand. "Henry. What can I do for you? Are you one of my students?"

"No sir." I reply. "I know you are the foremost expert on Greek Language and Studies and I want to pose a question to you. I have been doing research and studying Greek names and meaning. Would you happen to know what Africans were called by the Greeks?"

"What Africans were called by the Greeks? Aethiopians."

"That's correct. Dr. Bennett, the authority on Latin Studies adds. "Aethiopians."

Professor Bristol approaches a small chalk board in the office, smaller than the ones in the classrooms. He writes clearly every letter in the word. A E T H I O P I A N. "This is how it was spelled. Does that help with your question?" He asks.

"Yes." I fumble for a piece of paper in order to write what he has written. "This does satisfy my question. Thank you."

"I had trouble formulating purpose behind the third letter. This is why I consulted Professor Bristol. With his reply, it aided me in the drawing of a name. Alpha Phi Alpha."

"Alpha Phi Alpha." Nathaniel says.

I have already repeated the name in my mind twice before Nathaniel has had time to say it once. I can tell Nathaniel's response as his smile, that I have grown used to, covers his face.

"Yes," Henry answer. "Alpha Phi Alpha."

"I like that name." I state confidently. "Alpha Phi Alpha. Alpha Phi Alpha. I love the name and I know the others will take to it well just as we have."

"Yes, I know they will." Nathaniel states.

"Even C.C.?" Henry asks.

"You know C.C. better and are affiliated with him more than either of us." Nathaniel comments as he loses his smile.

"I do know C.C.'s position as he has made his stand quite clear. With a name for the society using Greek letters, it does give the appearance of a fraternity."

"Then our efforts are coming to fruition. Be they slow and steady nonetheless." I state. Henry is correct in his assessment. A name like Alpha Phi Alpha for our society is more in line with the fraternity idea that he, I and a few others share and s definitely sending us down the road to fraternal order. This path is not one we should shy away from. Instead, we need to forge forward and travel with confidence and purpose toward our goal. This is clearly a large step in that direction.

"Alpha Phi Alpha society." Nathaniel's approval of the name is showing as he continues to repeat it. "I do say gentlemen that I like the name a lot."

"What do you think about Alpha Phi Alpha fraternity?" I ask.

"I like that even better!" He replies with his familiar smile.

Today's meeting has nothing familiar about it. Not to me at least. Although Mr. Singleton is upon his usual routine, "Cleanliness before Godliness." and Mrs. Singleton must of the same, the routine for today's meeting is very peculiar.

"Robert, you seem very unlike yourself today. Is there something troubling you son?" Mrs. Singleton asks. As much as I am willing to share with this wonderful surrogate mother who has all but adopted not only myself and Morgan, but many of the others as well, I need to refrain and present my news as I had planned.

"No Ma'am, I am fine." I say with a convincing smile. "I would like things to be prepared for the meeting. I know how particular C.C. and Henry can be. Since the meeting is here at our residence, I would like to make sure all things are in order."

"Don't worry about that. We will make sure the facility is in order. Your friends will be arriving soon and we have prepared."

"Thank you Ma'am. That is reassuring." I reply,

"How are things progressing with your group? I think it is a fine thing that you boys are doing. Creating a study group and working so hard. I've heard of many students come and go but I have never heard the notion that you have come up with."

"We are doing well. Our ideas do not always match perfectly with one another and oftentimes we are led to strife. We return with a new sense of planning. All is well."

"It is very reassuring to hear. I believe Morgan has opened the door for someone. Maybe they are beginning to arrive."

I turn around and see that Morgan has indeed let Henry and Nat in. They are talking by the front door of the house and immediately I feel a sense of trepidation. My heart quickens. I need to feel at ease. These are brothers. They will understand. They will stand with me.

Before I have the opportunity to move to the next thought, Vertner, George Kelley and C.C. walk in together. They are talking amongst themselves like old friends, then turn their attention to Morgan who shakes Vertner's hand.

"Robert, how are you?"

"Henry, It's good to see you I am fine. How are you?"

"I am very well tan you. Looking forward to the conversation with the brothers today. Thank you for opening up the home for this one."

"Don't thank me. The appreciation need be directed at the gracious Singletons." I say.

"Of course. They are most hospitable always." Henry says with a smile. Henry doesn't comprehend how the conversation with the brothers is going to go today based on what I plan to present. Neither do I.

"Gentlemen, as punctual as I am," C.C. states loudly as to both announce and quiet the room, "I would like to begin. We have a few gents who have yet to arrive but I would like to begin talking." With that offering by C.C. the room quiets and everyone searches for a chair to claim. Morgan sits next to me.

"Are you well?" He leans toward me and asks quietly.

"Yes, I have to keep my wits and move forward."

"I understand." Morgan extends his hand to me. I take it and look directly into his eyes. This gesture of friendship means more to me than Morgan will ever realize.

The door opens and George Tompkins enters. He notices C.C. leading the meeting and finds a chair quietly.

"Gentlemen, I look forward to today's discussion. I have been doing diligent research and study on a few books. These books of interest I trust will capture the heart of the group as they have captured my attention. My... excuse me... our goal is to create a literary center where we can document not only school documents for other students but also offer selective reading materials." C.C. begins. "I wish to thank our hosts, Mr. and Mrs. Singleton for allowing us their home once again." Mr. Singleton smiles. Mrs. Singleton is in the kitchen preparing. "I wish to thank Morgan and Robert for making all reservations necessary for today's meeting."

This is my opportunity. We have met as a group several times between the fall, early semester and now. I know Professor Poindexter's routine and how he prefers to begin. I knew he would customarily show appreciation for the Singletons and to me and Morgan. In knowing this, I have prepared my statements to the moment he announces my name. A sense of nervousness overtakes me yet the call to move forward presses me.

"Thank you." Morgan says.

Mr. Singleton has already acknowledged with a nod of the head and a smile.

"Before we move further, I would like to make an announcement." I begin. Nervous feelings have left as I stand. Maybe they trouble more in a seated position but I feel at ease with my friends as I continue. "As all of you know or are aware by now, I am very much in love with Helen."

"Really? Who is Helen by the way?" Vertner asks with a smile. Vertner's question interrupts me and causes a flow of laughter to break into the room. His question is obviously a jest as he has met Helen several times. He has had tea in Charles' café with me and been forced to become privy to my love antidotes of Helen more than he cares to mention. His quirk has lightened the mood however and I need to remember to thank him.

"I am sure there aren't any other Helen Freeman Moores in Ithaca." I reply with a big smile. "My purpose for standing is..." Nervousness does affect a standing individual after all! "I have asked Helen Freeman Moore to marry me and she has accepted."

The silence only lasts one second but feels like one year.

"That is wonderful!" George Tompkins speaks first. "Good wishes to you two!"

"Thank you!" I reply with a handshake. Now each brother in the room is standing, shaking my hand, and patting my shoulder. I am lost in all of the congratulatory statements and well wishes I am more so relieved that I have told my best friends and solicited their support.

Charles comes into the open front door of the house. He seems a bit confused as to the commotion surrounding me.

"Charles, welcome. We have great news to share!" C.C. says.

"I apologize for my tardiness. I had to tend to a few items at the yard." he responds.

"Robert is getting married!" C.C. says without any thought to Charles being late.

Charles looks at me quickly with a very startled look.

"You're getting married?" he asks.

"Yes. Helen and I are to wed."

Charles' look changes immediately to a big smile, the largest smile I have seen Charles wear since I met him last semester.

"Congratulations my brother! When is the occasion?"

"This month. We wish to be with one another for the rest of our lives and we want to be wed as soon as possible. I should hope that all of you will be able to attend our festivities. They will be humble but lovely according to Helen and her family."

"I move that we all have to be in attendance!" George Kelley says loudly. Everyone laughs as Henry seconds and the motion carries.

"I most certainly will be there Bob. I would not miss it. Wild horses could not keep me back. A hurricane could not deter me. A raging barn fire would not hinder my attendance." Vertner says with a laugh.

I guess I am certain of two things: my feelings to be with Helen Freeman Moore and Vertner Tandy's and the others' attendance at our nuptial day.

"I'm very pleased that you were able to set aside time to meet with me."

"Most certainly. Honestly Morgan, it surprises me that you haven't visited my office until this point. Everyone else in the literary society has been to my office at least twice."

"I know. I must apologize."

"No need. Good to have you come by. What can I do for you?"

"I need to speak to you in the strictest of confidence. I have only revealed this to George Tompkins."

"Not Robert?"

"No. I had been meaning to talk to him but he informed me about he and Helen getting married and we weren't presented the opportunity to speak afterward."

"I understand. That was a surprise to me as well. Well what do you have on your mind?"

"It's my academic performance. I have been attempting to improve my study techniques and the amount of my reading time. I'm not performing well at all."

"Really? Why have you not brought this to my attention before?"

"I didn't want to alarm you or the group. I had oftentimes felt as if I would be able to improve on my own."

"Morgan... I wish you had used better judgment and brought this situation to me sooner. What are your scores?"

"I brought paperwork for your review. Since you are faculty, I thought that maybe you would be able to help."

"I am an instructor and you do know that but you have brought this to my attention well into the semester. I don't know how much help I can be. Let me see your paperwork."

"I have a few test papers. I have some writings that I would like to share with you."

"Are these from the instructor that you brought to our attention last semester? I can't recall his name."

"No. I did not fair well in his course either. These are not from him."

"Have you spoken directly with any of the professors?"

"No. I thought it more beneficial to speak with you first."

"Morgan, it's always best to speak directly with the individuals involved. Why are you... you need to set appointments right away. If you continue along this path, you will not be able to move forward with the rest of your class."

"I realize that."

"Apparently you do not. You should have brought this to someone's attention a lot sooner than this."

"I apologize."

"Which of these are for current classes and which are for last semester?"

"The two on top are last year and the others are this

semester."

"Morgan, this situation is not good at all!"

"No it isn't."

"I have spoken to everyone in the group over how many colored students come in and leave right out because of situations just like this. I have mentioned it time and time again. How could you sit there and allow this to grow as much as it has and not mention to me or at least Henry?"

"I grew afraid C.C. I didn't know what to do but try and do my best."

"Sometimes your best isn't good enough and you have to reach out for assistance. That is the entire purpose of our society. Have you not been paying attention during the meetings and discussions we have had? The responsibility has been repeated to the group on several occasions."

"I know it has. That is what has caused me to approach you today."

"We are approaching the close of the semester! We are passed the middle of the term! How do you expect me to help you run the race when the race is almost complete?"

"I don't know."

"Do you know if anyone else in the society is having similar complications?"

"I don't know."

"I need to speak with Henry right away. The status of the group is in question. There may be others holding similar secrets as you."

"I would think that everyone else in the society is moving forward better than I fair. I know Robert is doing well. The others seem to be doing equally as well."

"I will have to find out. Henry would more than likely know. I need to see what it is we can do for you."

"I had hoped that this situation would remain confidential."

"Confidential? We have to tell the others. That is what the literary society is based on. If we do not assist one another in our academic endeavors then there is no purpose behind our gatherings. You cannot be afraid of what others will think or say. If you keep this to yourself, you will not be matriculating with the others. It won't matter what they feel or say if that happens. You will no longer be at the university."

"I understand."

"I have spoken to students about similar situations before. I really had no thoughts toward any of my society students coming to me in such a manner."

"Once again I apologize for my reluctance to share this information. I chose the wrong path and hopefully will not live to regret it."

"I hope we all won't either. I like you Morgan and I am sure I can speak on behalf of the group. We do not wish to see any of our members fall by the wayside. I will do my best to help you. I just don't know how much I will be able to accomplish."

"It's very much appreciated C.C."

"I will be in touch shortly in regard to these matters."

"Thank you."

"'The Negro race, like all races, is going to be saved by its exceptional men.'" Henry reads. "' The problem of education then, among Negroes must first of all deal with the Talented Tenth; it is the problem of developing the best of this race that they may guide the mass away from the contamination and death of the worse, in their own race and other races. Now the training of men is a difficult and intricate task. Its technique is a matter of educational experts, but its object is for the vision of seers. If we make money the object of man training, we shall develop money makers but not necessarily men; if we make technical skill the object of education, we may possess artisans but not, in nature, men. Men we shall have only as we make manhood the object of the work of the schools, intelligence, broad sympathy, knowledge of the world that was and is, and of the relation of men to it, this is the curriculum of that higher education which must underlie true life. On this foundation we may build bread winning, skill of hand and quickness of brain, with never a fear lest the child and man mistake the means of living for the object of life.'"

"You read far better than you debate Sir Callis."

Henry and George laugh.

"What do you mean?"

"You bring out the point debating DuBois and Washington. A point that I must say holds little value in the scheme of opinion or fact based information. Yet you read DuBois' words so eloquently. I would have been more inclined to agree on your side of the debate had you read first, and presented your case later."

"I don't know Vertner, I may be able ot see past what you are seeing and understand Henry's point of view."

"Do you?" Henry asks curiously.

"Let me articulate as best I can, based on what you have thus far stated." George... George Tompkins that is, has always encouraged a feeling of mistrust in him. Not that I do not trust him with all that I have but I don't believe, in speaking with him, that he would freely speak his mind or thoughts in reference to the matter. Instead, he will wait cautiously within the conversation and present the side that best suits the conversation. "You had been inclined to follow a more Washington based view of the race, based on your early readings of Booker Washington's speeches and his position on this matter. Since coming to Cornell, you are more persuaded to agree with DuBois and his presentation; that education plays a vital role, even more than the normal labor of Washington.

"Yes, that is what I am referring, but with uncertainty." Henry responds.

"I have studied under Professor Washington and I certainly understand his mandate on the uplifting of the race." I state confidently. "To him, manual labor is the greatest means of advancement because it secures a place. There is always a need for field hands and always jobs to be maintained. His system does have its areas of merit. However, I can listen to the speech of DuBois and whether I agree with it or not,

I am of the Tenth that he speaks of. I am a Negro student matriculating in a White university. I am the very subject that he expounds on. That suits me. How does it suit the Negro that for means beyond his control can never aspire or obtain the educational opportunities afforded to us?"

"That doesn't stop one from attending. It didn't stop you." George says.

"No, it encouraged me. That only speaks well of Vertner. Not everyone else and other Negro students."

"It does speak well of Vertner and that is my point." Henry adds. "If even you, a former student and protégé of Washington can admit that even his nemesis has credit in his statements, then how many others, who are neither for nor against either, will see the merit in this as well? I don't know. I am just drawn to some of the statements and conclusions of his document."

"When was this presented?" George asks.

"Three years ago. Listen to this part. 'Education and work are the levers to uplift a people. Work alone will not do it unless inspired by the right ideals and guided by intelligence. Education must not simply teach work, it must teach life.' Profound and true!" Henry seems excited to read the Talented Tenth speech by W.E.B. DuBois. I think he is both impressed with DuBois' position on the matter and the notion that we are referred to as Negro college students throughout the document. DuBois pays heavy attention to the number of Negro college graduates and the likelihood that they will use the education presented to them in a collective means to move the race forward.

"That does sound like an incredibly intelligent stance. It is impressive." George says.

"So George, what is your position?" I ask smiling. I try my hardest to hide the smile and the true reason for me asking this question. It isn't to find out how George feels about the matter. It is more to test my personal conclusion that George will resort to what fits the conversation and what is convenient more than what he may feel or what may stir the emotions of those around.

"I don't know, what do you think Vertner?"

Smiling. "I understand DuBois' position. Even with my background. I am a walking and breathing testimony of what he is asserting. Even if I was of the mindset to not agree, I would be denying the fact that I am of this educational ten percent that DuBois speaks of."

"I agree," George adds, "one of the major thrusts in my life was to attend a university that would assist me in helping my own plight. Not my own personal plight but the plight of the race. Cornell will afford me the opportunity. That is why I chose to attend. So I agree with the lecture and can understand his viewpoint."

I laugh heartedly.

"What amuses you now?" George asks with a confused and skeptic look.

"Nothing George. Let me ask you another question." This question I know he will not waiver on and stands firm on his position, unlike the DuBois versus Washington debate, or any other debate presented him. "Literary society or fraternity?"

This time George has the laugh. "Literary society and nothing else... of course!"

"I call this meeting to order." C.C. announces as we take our proper places. "I trust everyone is prepared and ready to hear and focus on the tasks at hand. We have several items for discussion in this meeting and I want to drive forward with our agenda."

"Accolades to Nate for allowing us the use of his room for this meeting." Henry states.

"You're all very welcome." Nathaniel replies. "Make yourselves comfortable."

"Can I then light my cigar?" I ask jokingly. Everyone responds with laughter.

"Sure George, go right ahead. Just take it up with the

124

landlady once she knocks on the door from the smoke." Nathaniel adds with a smile.

After we settle, C.C. again takes command. "Gentlemen, I am excited about the impact this society will have in the future. As we come to a close of another semester, it only provides more insight as to what will lie ahead for us. Never before in my time here at Cornell did I leave a semester with so much anticipation. When the new students arrive in September, we will have something to offer them. A viable literary organ that will provide academic assistance and support. I want to develop a program of study focusing on American life in some way. Maybe a study of a designated foreign language. Something that broadens our minds and equips us all the more for our futures." C.C. ceases speaking immediately and opens a set of folded papers that are placed on Nathaniel's dresser. "Is anyone familiar with George Merriam?"

There is no response to C.C.'s question.

"George Merriam's book, The Negro and the Nation is a great collection of his thoughts pre and post Civil war era. Listen, let me read you an excerpt. 'It is difficult to write history, but it is impossible to write prophecy. We can no more tell what lies before us than the Fathers of the Republic could foresee the future a century ago. They little guessed that slavery, which seemed hastening to an end, would take new vigor from an increase of its profits, that stimulated by the material gain, a propaganda of religious and political defense would spring up, that a passionate denunciation and a passionate defense would gradually inflame the whole country. That meanwhile the absorption of the mass of citizens in private pursuits would blind them to the evil and peril, and prevent that disinterested comprehensive statesmanship which ought to have assumed as a common burden the emancipation of the slaves, that the situation would be exasperated by hostility of the sections and complicated by clashing theories of the national Union, that only by the bitter and costly war would a settlement be reached, and that emancipation being wrought by force and not by persuasion, would leave the master class convinced against its will, and a deep gulf between the races, whose spanning is still an uncertain matter, all this was hidden from the eyes of the wisest, a century ago. So is hidden from our eyes the outworking of the century to come.' When I came across this chapter, it really portrays my thoughts and vision for the upcoming semester and many semesters to come. None of us can foresee how far our efforts will reach. With the society we are instituting now, we have set in motion a viable reference tool for Negro students for years to come."

"I look forward to what we can accomplish as well." Vertner adds. "There is no limitation to what we can achieve if we work hard to accomplish our goals."

"Exactly." C.C. answers. "If your dream is to see this society as an actual organization where Colored students can come and pick up their reference materials, or receive the academic tutoring or assistance that they need, then let us work hard and create that dream." C.C. adjusts his papers and begins on another topic. "For the upcoming semester year, we need to establish and place in order the officers of our society. This will ensure viability into the coming term and steadfastness toward the group's ideals and goals."

"If I may..." Morgan states.

"Please." C.C. allows.

"I move to nominate Professor Poindexter as chair of the society for the upcoming school year."

"Thank you." C.C. says with a serious look.

"I second that." Henry adds.

Robert speaks forward. "I move that we keep Henry as our secretary if that does him well."

"It does sir, and thank you." Henry adds as he continues to write.

"I second the nomination for Henry and I move," Charles adds, "that George Kelley become the society treasurer."

"Me?"

"That is fine with me. I second the nomination." Vertner adds.

"Thank you gents," I reply, "thank you very much."

"This is a great step in the right direction gentlemen. This is the cornerstone that we need to build a solid house that will stand." C.C. says like a proud father.

"I think the foundation we are laying and the goals we are setting are more than achievable." Henry adds as he writes on his pad. Henry seldom looks up when he takes notes during our meetings. I have been privy to most of Henry's notes. He is meticulous and never misses anything. "We are well on course to generate the type of organization we envision."

"What we are missing is a name. An identifiable name in Ithaca" I add. My statement quickly quiets the room and for once, Henry looks up from his note taking.

"A name?" C.C. asks.

"Yes and I would like to present one. A name that I feel is extremely fitting. I cannot take credit for the origin of the letters or their meaning but the name Alpha Phi Alpha."

"Alpha Phi Alpha? Those are Greek letters." my namesake George states.

"Yes they are."

"But we have established that we are not a fraternity nor will be a fraternity. Why then would we want Greek letters to identify ourselves?"

"The name of the society," Henry defends, "has to have meaning. It has to have definitive meaning. This name was researched and found to fit well. Based on the ideals that Mr. Poindexter has provided, based on the foundation that has been laid thus far, and looking ahead as Messr. Poindexter so eloquently read, this is the name that accompanies our vision."

"Well if you have a dream right? I like it." Vertner says.

"I like it too." Robert adds. "Helen is going to love it!"

"Since when does your wife have a say in our affairs?" I ask jokingly which causes the room to erupt in laughter.

"I love the name Alpha Phi Alpha." Morgan states.

"I'm concerned fellows with the direction this name will propel us in." George Tompkins states in a serious tone. "We have argued this point before gentlemen. Every time we strongly decide what our intentions are with this society, this notion comes forth. Why does the attempt to create another direction and vision still exist? Greek letters indicate fraternal order. Everyone knows that. If we are to..."

"Actually George, I don't think it is a bad notion." C.C. says to the surprise of myself and I'm sure most others in the room. "Alpha Phi Alpha Society. At least we can own this name informally."

George Tompkins doesn't seem to know if he should exist beside himself or not. This is the first instance in which Poindexter and Tompkins are not in agreement and it has taken George by surprise.

I look at Henry who is staring back at me. We two awaiting the next response by someone... anyone. George Tompkins is the first to respond. He responds by standing and excusing himself from the room. There is a deafening quiet which follows the sound of the door being closed and George's footsteps going down the hallway.

"George Tompkins may be the sole individual in our group not in favor." Charles says. "I too like the name."

"I suppose Alpha Phi Alpha doesn't suit George well." Vertner says laughing.

"Not so!" I say with a smile. "Alpha Phi Alpha suits me very well! Very well indeed!"

A

Well this is it! How noble a place! How fitting a residence! Cornell is very different than Union... Ithaca is very different than Richmond. Nonetheless, this is home; my new home. A new place for new life, new learning, new journeys and I approach with vigor and anticipation. My accommodations are modest at best yet comfortable.

"Mr. Jones, I trust you will find your living quarters adequate." The new landlady states.

"Yes Ma'am. Thank you, it is well." I say as I begin shifting, in my mind at least, how my new furniture is to be situated.

"I will leave you alone to your things and your preparation." She closes the door upon her exit. She seems to be a nice lady but has set the ground rules in our relationship up front and clear. There are quiet hours, what she deems as study hours, and resting hours. Seem to all equate to quiet surroundings to me. She also has declared no beverages of alcohol, tobacco products or card playing take place in her rooms. That will suit me fine if those are the rules. My upbringing dictates the same manner, albeit not always followed. Nonetheless in circumstances such, to oblige is not impossible or improbable.

No sooner than I turn to begin to fully secure and acquire my new home, she knocks on my new door again. I open the door but to my surprise it isn't the landlady.

"I suppose you are one of my newest roommates." The fellow making the remark is a tall stout gentleman with full cheeks. Wearing glasses, he has a distinguished way about him yet his smile is more comical than inviting. "Vertner Woodson Tandy is the name."

"Eugene Kinckle Jones." I reply with an outstretched hand and matching smile. "Nice to meet you."

"Pardon but what kind of a name is Kinckle?" His tone is almost of ridicule but his smile remains warm.

"It's a family name. On my mother's side."

"Oh well, pardon me for asking."

"Fine. Many call me Kinckle but most call me Gene." I reply.

"So be it. I will know you as Eugene until I know you further."

"Indeed."

"Tell me something about yourself that I would not gather at first glance."

This Vertner is quite a fellow. "I hail from Richmond. Are you familiar with the south?"

"Yes but I have spent time in the very south. Alabama."

"Really? Born and raised?"

"No, no," Vertner responds. "Educated in college before transferring here."

"Then we have that in common. I have attended Virginia Union University before coming to mingle with the White boys." Vertner laughs with me. Virginia Union is an all Black university well known for its background in religious education. The transition from a campus such as Union to Cornell can be quite an experience so I've been forewarned.

"My training is from Tuskegee. I completely understand your viewpoint on the adjustment. Trust me I made the transition last year. Quite a year it was!" Vertner and I seem to have a lot in common.

"You may have to assist me in the change. I was told that White boys may bite."

Vertner smiles. "No, they only bark."

"How has it been for the Negro students here? Are you familiar with any in particular?" I ask. The question actually is one that I have thought of well before I began my journey to Cornell and Ithaca. Would I be able to meet other students with like interests? Would there be camaraderie among other Negro students?

"Some of the Negro students and I have formed a group, the Alpha Phi Alpha Society for just the purpose you are questioning."

"Alpha Phi Alpha Society?" I ask, interrupting Vertner. What type of group is that?"

"We exist as a literary society, here to assist other Negro students in their academics and their adjustment to college life. We held several meetings beginning last year and ending in the spring with a few events in the city. We closed the school year with a banquet in June. Currently we have seven students and one faculty advisor."

"Really? My father is a professor of Greek studies! My knowledge of such matters may deem very useful to your society!"

"Your father is a professor of Greek?" Vertner excitedly asks.

"Homiletics and Greek studies. He is a minister and teacher."

"I think you would fair well with our group. You need to be introduced to Henry Callis. His father is a preacher man too! Henry is the one who came up with the name of the society; Alpha Phi Alpha. I'm certain he will find your knowledge of Greek matters useful."

"Henry Callis."

"Yes. If you are willing to attend, we are having a meeting of the society and you can meet the others as well. As well as our president, Professor Poindexter."

"What takes place at the meetings?"

Vertner laughs before he answers. "Arguments and disruptions." He laughs again. "We have had disagreements but the sentiment is one of serving our fellow Negro students and collectively uniting for the common good."

"When is the meeting? I would like to attend with you if that is possible."

"I'll contact Henry and find out the exact date and location, then notify you."

"Thank you for the information. I look forward to it."

"Certainly Kinckle, certainly!"

Charles welcomes us with outstretched arms and warm hugs. "Helen how are you?"

"Doing well Charles, thank you for asking. You?" Helen responds with a big smile.

"All is well. How is the baby fairing?"

I choose to answer as I assist Helen in taking her seat. "We are looking forward to our family with much excitement."

"Good! I believe we all will be anxious. The Ogle family is growing and that is a wonderful and blessed thing." Charles smiles. "Can I get you coffee?"

"I'll take one, thank you."

"Helen?" Charles asks cordially.

"No, I'm fine. Thank you."

Charles smiles and takes off to get my cup.

"It's good to see Charles again. It's been too long since we've visited this place." Helen says.

"You're right. The summer months have gone by quickly and with the baby on the way and the new semester, the time has swiftly passed."

"Yes it has." Helen takes my hand and smiles at me. "I love you Robert."

"I love you too Helen Ogle."

Charles returns with a hot cup of coffee for me and the cinnamon wafers that he knows Helen prefers. She smiles as she is accommodated.

"Thank you sir."

"Please alert me if you need more." Charles says as he sits down. He turns his attention to me. "Have you spoken to anyone else? C.C. or the Georges? Henry?"

"No I haven't. I'm looking forward to our first meeting for that reason." I reply. "I suppose you have yet to hear about Morgan Phillips."

"I haven't spoken to anyone about Morgan or anyone else. What is it?"

"Morgan is not returning to Cornell." I say solemnly.

"Really? What happened to him?" Charles asks.

"He was never able to recover. It occurs all too frequently, just as C.C. warned. I just wasn't aware that it would happen to my best friend."

"It's not your fault Robert." Helen says. She's told me this before.

"She's right Robert. Every man is responsible for his own way."

"I know. I realize that. I just wish it hadn't happened." I offer. My statement leads to a silence... an uncomfortable silence. "I'm looking forward to seeing everyone next week. Especially Henry." I break the silence with a slight change of subject. With the foundation laid last semester, we have tremendous momentum to move forward."

"I agree. I took some of the summer weeks and read of slave narratives and also race relations. I plan to share with the society upon our return to regular scheduled meetings."

"What are some of the things you read?" I ask after blowing on my coffee.

"I read of cases of segregation. There was a case in Kansas. The school building burned and a father attempted to have his son attend the newly built brick building. The Negro students were made to go back to the old edifice. The son is only 8 years old. I studied a case where the school established two sessions, one for white students and one for Negro students to avoid students attending at the same time."

"This is good material for the society's meeting." I say.

"The Alpha Phi Alpha Society. I sure like the name." Helen says smiling.

"She says it all the time." I confess on my wife's behalf.

Charles smiles. "I certainly hope other students at Cornell take to it as Helen has."

"I'm certain Society will be well received." I say confidently.

"How was your time away George?"

"Busy with thought, contemplation and planning. Yours?"

"Consumed with the same. More of the DuBois papers and study."

"Henry Callis the philosopher." I laugh at George's claim that I am a philosopher. He and I both know that I would accept no such claim. Humorous as it may be.

"George Biddle Kelley the planner!" I return. We get an even better laugh from that claim. "So what are your plans for the semester?"

"For me or Alpha Phi Alpha?"

"Is there a distinction sir?" I ask with a smile.

"My plan is..." George pauses as if to consider his plan. "...the plan is to proceed in two ways. First to draw attention to Alpha Phi Alpha and encourage Negro students to participate in our activities. Second, to draw even more information from Theta Beta Pi. Some of its members have agreed to share with me their by-laws in helping me... us, with ideas for our group. Then, we need to fully establish ourselves as a fraternal organization. Just like you, I, Nat, Robert have spoken of."

"I agree except for the fact that you present one major dilemma."

"What is that?" George asks curiously.

"You presented that your plan is twofold and you mentioned three items."

George laughs. "Henry Callis the witty."

"I do want to present to the group the idea to do a banquet of our own. Much like what I witnessed early last semester. With assistance, we could do the same."

"I hope so and I look forward to that." George admits.

"Something of that caliber would be tremendous for us and draw much attention to our cause!"

"I know Professor Poindexter would be willing to oversee a project like this."

George immediately becomes quiet.

"You don't agree on Professor Poindexter?"

George ponders before he answers. "I think C.C. is a great leader and a great man of vision. I know however that he has no interest in hearing of our requests or goals. He would sooner abandon us as members and start with a new band of students then to admit and be a part of any fraternity effort."

"I don't know. I think we can convince him of the merit of our efforts and have him as a solid force." I return.

"I don't think so. With the hold he has on some of us... Charles, George, Morgan, it seems as if a stalemate would ensue forever. We need more students to join our efforts and recognize our efforts."

I consider what George is saying and realize that he is correct. I would appreciate the participation of a powerful visionary like Professor Poindexter. With him at the helm, Alpha Phi Alpha could reach and change the course of several students at Cornell. As George says, C.C. is set in his ways and would probably give up the idea before conforming to the idea of Alpha Phi Alpha Fraternity.

"I know you revere Professor Poindexter," George continues, "but the relationship that he maintains with most of the... society... is one of intimidation. Most in our band will not speak what they truly feel because of the pressure to agree. Not even you can deny that."

"No I can't deny it. You're right once again. George Biddle Kelley, the always correct."

"What did you mention your name is again?"

"Lemuel. Lemuel Graves." He shakes my hand so heartily that it feels as if his intent is to shake it right off my arm.

"Pleased to meet you Mr. Murray." He says enthusiastically.

"Pleased to meet you too and please call me Nathaniel."

"Sure."

"Where are you from?"

"North Carolina. Raleigh to be exact."

"North Carolina! I've never been." I reply.

"It's very nice. Not like upstate New York. Not at all."

"So has the adjustment been a difficult one for you?"

"No. I had prepared myself for the move. I do like Cornell and I look forward to my studies. I'm happy that you took the time to introduce yourself. I don't know many students here. Especially the Colored students. Seems as if we are in various places across the university."

Lemuel's statement causes me to look across the crowded campus of Cornell. We have chosen to speak outside as this is one of the last warm days in the transition from summer to fall. Looking across the campus on a day like today lays heavy claim and validity to Lemuel's claim. There are more than several White students walking about, talking amongst themselves. Every instance or so, you may see a Negro student. Even those chances are not nearly as likely as the former.

"The purpose of the Alpha Phi Alpha Society as I mentioned to you before is to bond the very students we speak of and unite us in a common effort for mutual benefit. Scholarship is our mandate. We want to ensure everyone has the greatest opportunity affordable for their progression and matriculation." I say. "The group members are of one mind on this and are heavily concerned with inviting others to join our efforts." As these words leave me, I consider what I have said. In one instance, I am exactly correct in that the group is concerned with the matriculation of our vastly separated brothers. We are not however on one accord on how to go about this. The notion of a literary society and of a fraternity coexists neither being able to remove the other at any given time. As one takes precedence, the other triumphs later. The struggle has been equally matched since the beginning with no clear end in sight.

"When you and I met at the opening of the semester, I was curious as to this Alpha Phi Alpha Society that you mentioned. The more we discuss, the more I am willing to meet the members and lend a hand. I agree with the mandates and the purposes you have laid before me. I look forward to meeting the others."

"If you have one mind toward the advancement of college men, then you are in line with our cause and welcomed to join us in meeting. I am certain the others will be equally interested in meeting you as you are of them."

For the first time I feel intimidated walking into Professor Poindexter's office. My palms are wet and I am noticeably nervous. I have felt nervous around him before, especially when he pursues his case against George or Robert or even Vertner. Since I have aligned myself with the literary society idea and fully believe and promote its premise, I don't ever fear C.C. in that instance. I more feel sorry for the others who continually push the plan for a fraternity and since I've been at the core of some of the most heated exchanges I have ever seen, I myself am nervous that it might turn against me. It never has.

Today may promise to be different in that C.C. has chosen to disagree with me on a significant part of our foundation; the name of the society. Maybe it was a mistake to voice my opinion so quickly when the name Alpha Phi Alpha was announced. I chose to do that with the full confidence that C.C. would be in disagreement as well. Little did I know that he and I would be on different sides on the issue. It seemed as if I stood alone. Professor Poindexter has called me to his office. I am sure he wishes to discuss my outburst and abrupt departure from the meeting and all things Alpha Phi Alpha. When I received his message, I saw the fiery side that debates so heavily with the other George now coming down on me. I have not looked forward to this meeting.

"George, good of you to make it." C.C. says with an outstretched hand. He walks into his office with an urgent sense as if he is late for his own meeting.

"Good to see you Professor."

"Please sit down." He offers as he quickly takes his seat and seems to be down to business. "How was your summer off George?" I'm quite surprised that he has started with pleasantries.

"It was..." I actually pause to consider my answer, making sure I am not setting myself in for one of C.C.'s debate tactics, "...was pleasant. I had some time to think about choices and my visions for the future. Summer offers me a much needed break from classroom and campus."

C.C. continues to lean forward in his chair, a posture I have only witnessed from him in debate circumstances. "I understand. George," he is quick to move to the purpose, "I was rather disappointed in your abrupt removal last semester. We held a banquet to end the semester that you were unaware of."

"I have been told."

"The banquet was the culmination of our efforts from the previous semester through the spring. Robert informed us that he and his new bride are expecting their first child."

"Really?" I hadn't been told that. "That is wonderful"

"Yes it is. I hope it doesn't interfere with his studies though. Raising a family is a tremendous responsibility on anyone."

"Yes, I'm sure."

"You leaving the final meeting left you unaware."

I have thought about my responses today as soon as I got word that C.C. wanted to meet with me. I have gone through my thoughts and pondered what it is I would respond with. In my mind, I have envisioned him asking me several questions under several different circumstances. The responses that I have prepared however may throw me into conflict with him if I answer honestly. The one situation I would like to avoid is a debate or a disagreement with C.C.

"I understand that and agree. However, the name of this society... being named Alpha Phi Alpha reserves me and sets me in strong disagreement with the purpose we have set."

C.C. leans back, not to relax but to listen.

"If we are stating that we are against the idea of a fraternity, and that a fraternity has no place in the mindset of the Negro college student, then we cannot have any resemblance of a fraternity. Especially in our name. A name like Alpha Phi

Alpha, three Greek letters with no apparent meaning... it says fraternity. It is counterproductive to our efforts and all that we and those interested in maintaining the literary cause have fought for.

Poindexter is silent.

"I was taken aback sir, at your response." That was not a rehearsed statement nor was it calculated prior. As soon as I state it however, I regret it.

"The fact that those who are insistent with this fraternity and have chosen a name like Alpha Phi Alpha is not my concern nor should it be yours! My concern is a course of study for this semester! My concern is a foreign language that we should undertake! My concern is the fact that one of our members isn't returning to Cornell this semester!"

"What! Who?" I had no idea that someone isn't returning! This is startling news!

"Had you been with me and in contact, you would've known as well! George, this is not about what name they choose! This is about you leaving our effort! I always counted on you and your vote!"

C.C. immediately stands and takes a book that is placed on his desk. He doesn't open it. He gazes down at me "I have study matters to tend to. If you would please pardon me..."

No more need be said. I stand and walk out of C.C.'s office with the same sentiment that I walked from Nathaniel Murray's room in June.

I knew that as soon as I entered the house for the meeting, I would be overjoyed to see everyone. To this point, I hadn't seen Robert, Charles Chapman or Nathaniel. As I enter the home of Mr. Newton, now a familiar dwelling, I see several faces that I do not recognize. Two speaking with Vertner. I do remember James who attended a few meetings last semester and showed a great deal of interest in Society.

"Henry!"

I turn immediately and am greeted by Charles. "Charles, how are you? It's good to see you!"

"Great to see you too!" he says as he takes my hand. "Good to see the spirit is still alive in us to meet and conduct the business at hand."

"Indeed! I am very excited about what this New Year will bring. We have a strong foundation with great vision."

"Apparently a few new interested men in our group." We both look around the room at the unfamiliar faces.

"Do you know any of them?" I ask.

"No. Do you?"

"No. I have yet to be introduced." As I look around once again, I'm approached by George Kelley.

"Henry."

"George, good to see you. Looking for a great meeting to start us off."

George smiles yet remains well within the confines of his strict composure. "Most certainly. I believe we all are anxious."

"C.C. has just entered." Charles says. "Time to get to business."

"Has anyone seen Morgan?" George asks.

"I haven't seen him."

"Robert informed me that Morgan has not returned this semester." Charles answers.

"Really!" I say as C.C. makes his rounds and comes my way.

"Hello Mr. Callis. How are you?" C.C. says with an outstretched hand.

"I'm fine sir, how are you?"

"Ready to get started. I'm well equipped and well prepared. Are you ready?"

"Yes I am."

"We can call the meeting to order then. I have a lot to discuss so let us begin."

Charles and George take seats and C.C. proceeds in calling the meeting to order. "Gentlemen, I move that this meeting of Alpha Phi Alpha be called to order. Myself, President C.C. Poindexter presiding, Henry Callis, Secretary. Gentlemen, we have a lot to discuss this evening but before we get into agendas and formalities, let me be the first to say it is good to be back and to see almost everyone. Welcome back to Cornell. You brothers have made it into the new school year. Unfortunately our friend Morgan Phillips is no longer enrolled as a student at Cornell."

"He's not?" James asks almost as an outburst.

"No. He was not able to recover academically so he remained home in Washington." Robert explains.

"We will miss him but gentlemen, understand the plight. This happens all too often and the situation is too common. If anyone else in this set of members ever has academic or any other difficulties, please bring it to my attention."

I am not certain if the news of Morgan not returning has silenced the room or the charge to alert Professor Poindexter in the event of failed academics. Either way, everyone awaits C.C.'s next declaration.

"Before we go any further, I do see new faces in the room which pleases me a great deal. Please stand and give us your names quickly."

"Two men stand at the same time, notice one another, then sit at the same time which causes laughter to break out in the room. One concedes to the other.

"Good evening, my name is Gordon Jones and it is my pleasure to be making your acquaintances." He takes his seat.

"Gentlemen, my name is Eugene Jones and I was invited by Mr. Vertner Tandy. Thank you."

This must be the new student that Vertner spoke of. He has a background history in Greek studies and can be helpful in solidifying for me the name of our group. He is greeted and takes his seat as well."

"Good evening gentlemen. My name is Lemuel Graves. I am excited about being at Cornell and about attending this meeting. Thank you for the warm welcome."

"Thank you all and you are welcome. You will find our mandates and vision is to pursue scholarship and the academic success of all around us. We have worked hard to attain what we have thus far and we look forward to you working with us." C.C. changes his tone. "Over the summer months, I read manuscripts and prepared various readings for this group to place on our agenda as literary projects and courses of study. Daniel Murray is the son of a freedman and has compiled an extensive list of books and pamphlets by Negro authors. In his own words, 'The object in this effort is to secure a copy of every book and pamphlet in existence, by a Negro author, the same to be used in connection with the Exhibit of Negro authorship at the Paris Exposition in 1900, and later placed in the Library of Congress.' What an outstanding feat he has attempted and I have been able to secure several of these manuscripts. This literary society can now choose what we plan to present for this year as our direction and course of study." C.C. states proudly. "We will ensure the sustaining of this group and all of its members from this meeting further."

Vertner raises his hand and is acknowledged. "What has become or what is our decision regarding George Tompkins? Has anyone heard from him or is he in a similar instance as Morgan?"

"I have spoken to George personally and he has strong opinions and views about this group. I applaud his stance and anyone's stance on either side when you are willing to take hold of a position. I am more than certain that we will hear from George very soon." C.C. says assuredly. An answer that surprises me as much as George Tompkins' abrupt exit surprised me last semester.

"I applaud you Professor Poindexter on your efforts at securing this reading material for the group." I offer. "I am certain this list of materials will prove to be useful to our members as the semester continues."

"It will prove to be very useful." C.C. affirms. I will submit the entire list to you Henry for your documentation efforts."

"Thank you sir."

"Do we need to establish for this group regular meeting

days and times?" Charles asks.

"Yes. That is an item on our agenda." C.C. answers.

"I move that the meetings be held on Tuesday evenings." Vertner states. Robert seconds the motion. I record the vote and the motion carries. The visitors observe.

George asks to be recognized and is. "I would like to propose a planning committee for a formal banquet."

"A banquet?" C.C. asks.

"Yes. I've spoken to some of my friends and Henry has informed some of us of his friends at Sigma Alpha Epsilon and how they went forward with their banquet. It was on a grand scale."

C.C. turns in my direction yet I continue to take notes.

"I've witnessed these events at Sage. Splendid and fine events, every one of them. I've worked the last two fraternity dinners at Sage and know all there is to do in preparing."

James Morton has just reminded us of his working relationship on campus with the dining facilty and with the events and functions that they host. Attending the Sigma Alpha Epsilon banquet last semester was a great means in planning a similar function. Yet having someone like James with direct knowledge or Charles with expertise in serving and preparing of meals, or George Kelley in waiting, all afford us a genuine pathway to making a profound statement at Cornell. Alpha Phi Alpha Society has all that it needs to conduct an event on the same scale as some of our colleagues on campus... the White fraternities.

"I would prefer gentlemen if we discuss the items on the agenda that Henry and I have worked hard to have ready for this meeting." C.C. clearly does not want to entertain thoughts of a banquet similar to those conducted by the fraternities on campus.

"I move we vote." Robert says in a clear defiant move to C.C. Even Poindexter would applaud the effort to conduct business in a meeting. As President, he has always encouraged this group to resolve a matter with the proper sign and procedure, with a vote. That philosophy, which has been adhered to by his demand, may prove to be the undoing of his tight hold on the sway of the vote with sentiment changing and George Tompkins absent.

"I second the motion on the floor to vote." George states boldly. With reluctance yet confidence... "All in favor of a fall banquet..."

Before C.C. has the opportunity to complete the motion, it carries.

"A banquet! When?" Helen excitedly asks me.

"October, we are still deciding on the date." I reply.

"What a splendid affair that will be!"

"I believe so." I respond. "Henry took the time to describe the fraternity banquet that he attended last semester. He described it as a grand affair. A spectacular menu and James Morton all but guaranteed a fine course for our event as well. We also spoke of George being the toastmaster and we were all given topics for speeches."

Helen smiles brighter. "Really? What are you going to speak on?"

"Welcome brother."

Helen smiles her familiar smile of approval, then leans back and rubs her stomach. "That is wonderful Robert and you will fair well!"

"Well I hope you plan on being in attendance with me."

"I don't know, I have not been feeling too well as of late as I am far along in the pregnancy."

"Yes I know." I respond. I do know. If the banquet is held in mid to late October, Helen will be well past seven months and my goal has been to keep her inside and with as little strain as possible. "I agree with you wholeheartedly."

"I would love to be there and will come if I feel up to it."

"Think no more on it and we will decide when the time approaches."

Helen smiles at me.

"The speeches will be exciting. I know that this is some of the group's method to gain momentum for the fraternal idea."

"What do you mean?" Helen asks.

"The idea for a fraternity is growing stronger, yet still in opposition to those who are in favor of literary society. When the vote was taken to organize this banquet effort, it was clearly more along the lines of the fraternity. As the plans began to crystallize that evening, more ideas arose that could possibly solidify the efforts for fraternity. Nathaniel suggested that George Kelley be toastmaster. This led to the various members choosing their speaking topics. I found it quite amusing at some of the topics in light of our debates."

"What do you mean? Do you remember any?"

"I don't remember them all but I do know that George Kelley's topic is why organize. Professor Poindexter's topic is ideals. The others I cannot recall."

"How appropriate!" Helen says laughing. I laugh with her.

"Indeed! As I mentioned, quite amusing. I believe some will deliberately use these small platforms as leverage toward their case. Whether their case be for the fraternity or not."

"Will you?" Helen asks sarcastically and smiles coyly.

"I would rather deliver a speech based on my heart's love for you. That would make for a convincing argument!"

We join in laughter.

Helen takes my hand. "In that instance, pregnant or not, I wouldn't miss your speech for the world!"

"I've heard so many good things about you Henry that I feel that I know you."

I shake Eugene's hand and welcome him in. He is a dashing fellow with good looks and a sharp manner about him. "I'm glad you are familiar with me. I suppose you can assist me in becoming equally as familiar with you."

He smiles as we walk inside and sit down.

"I actually have heard good things in regard to you as well. I have spoken with Vertner." I state.

"Ah, Vertner. You know, where I'm from there wouldn't be enough room for both Vertner and I. The small city of Richmond can only handle one practical joker at a time." Eugene says.

"As can we. We barely maintain."

Both Eugene and I laugh.

"What has he shared with you on my behalf?" He asks.

"Vertner approached me in his familiar fashion and stated, 'Henry, oh Henry, I have a unique fellow. Gene I call him. I would like to present for you acquaintance.'"

Eugene laughs as I mimic Vertner's voice.

"He went on to tell of your former college in Virginia and your knowledge of Greek matters. That became intriguing to me."

"Yes and equally intriguing to me when I heard the name of the Society and was told that you had a hand in the naming of it."

"I spoke with a professor of Greek literature to find out from him what the Greeks called the Africans. I have written some items on the name in which I derive both the meaning and purpose behind our group."

"That is outstanding! Do you mind if I read what it is you have put together?

"I don't mind at all. I would prefer that you did in order to help assist the group with this purpose." As I get up to retrieve my paperwork, Eugene continues.

"You know, in Egyptian life there is evidence of Negro influence as well as in the life of the mixed races of the Northern African coast."

I turn back toward him with the paperwork. "Are you familiar with Egypt and its culture and customs?" Eugene Jones is becoming more useful, intriguing and becoming!

147

"Egyptology. My father touches on it in his studies so I am familiar. I find the culture interesting."

"I had been curious," as I take my seat, "as to some of the customs and how we could possibly incorporate cultural references into our theme." I hand him my papers.

As he begins to look through what I have written, I study his demeanor more closely. Eugene Kinckle Jones is a thinker. He analyzes. He is a tremendous asset to this group. He takes his time in studying my attempt and doesn't respond until he has read, probably twice, and has a clear understanding.

"I am impressed with what you have come up with Henry. Very impressed and I believe we can build on what you have begun."

"I am relieved to hear you say that. I prefer to know where I am walking and not walk in complete darkness. Sometimes it seems as if we as a group are wandering with no direction. Then other meetings sound with purpose, vision and concise clarity. Then there are times when one objective replaces the other prior objective or one mood dominates another mood."

"The making of anything great!" Eugene says laughing. I smile with him. "From what I gather of your writings," he glances back at my papers, "you have complied as much as you could and put together a well thought out foundation for the Society. Hopefully some of what I have learned will prove to be useful in your efforts."

"Where does your knowledge of Greek matters or Greek letters or fraternities begin?"

"Well... I know that Philip the Second was a wealthy leader and spared no expense in ensuring that his court would be the finest in the world. His militia, his empire, his philosophers. He imported Aristotle himself to personally tutor his son Alexander."

"Alexander the Great." I offer.

"Precisely. Phillip was a man of culture and the effects of what he instilled in his people reached far beyond the borders of Greece. His influence touched Egypt all the way to its south border and as far east as India. Since many of the people who were touched by this culture were not originally of the heritage, much of the dialect was more simple and not as course as someone born in Greek lineage."

"It became almost like a broken language." I state more than ask, yet not knowing.

"Yes."

"How did you learn that?

Eugene smiles. "My father is an instructor and I was enrolled at Virginia Union. Much of the curriculum gears toward the doctrine of strict Christianity. My father also being a reverend."

"Mine too." I offer.

"Yes, I can tell in your stately walk." Eugene laughs at his own sarcasm as do I. He returns. "The common or broken language derived from this ancient Greek is called Koine and is the language that the Gospels were originally composed in."

"Fascinating. I didn't know that."

"There's probably a lot more we can learn from one another Henry. I am more than willing to contribute to what you have begun here. You have laid a solid foundation and it's clear. I look forward to helping you and this group move forward."

I look forward to what he will bring to this group. A tremendous addition is Eugene Jones to Alpha Phi Alpha.

"Fellows," I begin, "I am very much pleased with the idea Robert offered to meet outside of any new members. Decisions need to be made and questions need to be raised and answered without their knowledge."

"Vertner is right." George supports my opening statement. "We need to consider each person applying for membership and finalize how to conduct their initiation efforts."

When this meeting was called and finalized, I thought it was an appropriate idea. I, like I am sure most of the others, am very curious as to how this is going to be considered. We have several names to consider and a decision need be made as to how to manage. This is obviously a first venture and we have no guide in which to reference. We have been traveling along a road of ideas being presented and implemented.

"What ideas have you heard from your friends George?" Robert asks his question carefully, recognizing the reaction he may receive from the presiding officer, Professor Poindexter. There is no reaction as George responds quickly.

"In numerous conversations with the members of Theta Beta Pi, the best thing to do is to have the initiation ceremony during our banquet. We need to discuss each name in detail and decide whether these men are worthy of our ranks."

"Well let us discuss! We need to first talk about Gordon Jones. He lives in the house and the man has been running behind me and asking me questions since he attended our meeting! I almost have to hide in my own room from his enthusiasm!" My statement causes everyone to laugh as I assume they consider someone of my size running from someone of Gordon's size. I laugh myself.

"He probably contains just the zest and life that we need in building this..." Robert pauses as he thinks of what to define this group as, "this... Society."

"That stands good for him then. He seems to be willing to take an active part in this and I recommend him for membership." George suggests.

"I would like to cast my favor for James Morton." Charles states. "We all know and have liked James from when he responded to the call last semester. He has attended meetings as his work schedule has allowed."

"Yes, I believe James is heavily concerned with the advancement of our agenda." C.C. points out. "I've spoken to him on more than one occasion and he expresses to me an earnest desire for the goals and vision of the Society. I have always been impressed with his stature."

"I see the potential in James. He and I spoke until the morning daylight hours once." George adds. "Now that he is enrolled as a student, there are no further hindrances to his full acceptance in our group."

Our group is in agreement on both Gordon and James.

"I'm excited about recommending Eugene Kinckle Jones." Henry states next. "We sat and had a conversation about the name that we have attached to this group and we spent due diligence on the vision and meaning. Gene is quite equipped and knowledgeable about several topics as it concerns us. He comes sharp, witty and prepared to work within a committee for this organization."

"Speaking of which," George states loudly and confidently, "we have never voted or duly accepted our name. Henry proposed it with reservation some time ago... last semester. We do have a need to make our name an official status of this group. I assume everyone has been in favor of that name. The opposition at the time of the meeting was George Tompkins."

I glance at Professor Poindexter for his reaction. He has been quiet throughout the meeting thus far and remains as such, other than the routine responsibilities of the presiding officer.

"I move that the Society be known by the Greek letters Alpha Phi Alpha." George proclaims.

The motion is properly seconded by me and the motion carries.

"I move that the colors old gold and black be adopted as the colors of Alpha Phi Alpha Society." Robert says smiling.

"How long have you had that in mind, waiting to pounce upon us?" I ask laughing. Everyone laughs as they see as I have that Robert was anxiously waiting to propose that motion. The motion carries.

"I am actually pleased that George Tompkins is brought up. I want to open for discussion." C.C. says. This is the most he has said all evening and the mood quickly shifts to the serious tone that usually resonates in our meetings until heated debate breaks forth. "George is interested in continuing and moving forth with this literary society. We have had our conversations and he is looking to join committees, work with research material, organize events, or whatever else the call is from the Society for its members."

"I thought we had lost our brother George." Henry says.

"I thought the same thing." George Kelley states.

"I have spoken with him and like I am mentioning, he is more than willing to move forward with the literary society... the Alpha Phi Alpha Society." C.C. replies.

"So how do you propose we recommend him?" I ask.

"Can we receive George as an old member?" Nathaniel asks.

"Yes. That is a good recommendation." C.C. states. "I move that George Tompkins be received as an old member." C.C.'s motion carries.

"Should we then include Tompkins in the initiation activities that I have scheduled for the others?" I ask.

"No, I don't suggest he be subject to an initiation. George is one of us. He was here in the very beginnings of this Society. If he has a desire to return, he should be allowed." Henry states.

"If you hear of the activities I have planned for these victims... candidates... you may reconsider!" I say smiling.

Everyone laughs at my joke except Poindexter and Charles.

"From my committee gentlemen," I try and regain the composure of the meeting, "Charles has notified me of the cost to secure the required location of the banquet and initiation."

"Yes, the Odd Fellows Hall can be secured for Tuesday for the ceremonies at the cost of one dollar and fifty cents." Charles says.

"Very well." C.C. comments. "Vertner, you will be taking care of that as Treasurer?"

"Yes sir."

"Good. It seems gentlemen that we are set for the first banquet of the Alpha Phi Alpha Society." With that proclamation, C.C. Poindexter takes up his belongings and exits the room.

"I was notified late Tuesday night. How about you?" Gordon

asks.

"I was as well." I reply.

"Tuesday? I wasn't notified until late Saturday night." Lemuel adds.

"Late Saturday?" I ask. "Saturday past? Two days ago?"

"Yes."

I wonder if it means anything that Lemuel was called to be a part of the initiation after Gordon and I. "Well at least you have been called Lemuel. That is the most important element at the immediate moment."

"Thank you Eugene. I can say that I am intimidated, yet happy to be here."

"I think we all are rather anxious." I say. I attempt to ease fears but Lemuel is correct. I have heard, as I am sure they have as well, of some of the tactics of initiation ceremonies and rituals. Many of the fraternities and social organizations have attempted to recreate ancient passage processes to intimidate or injure their prospective candidates. I do know that Henry Callis has ties with one of the White fraternities. I don't recall which one. If they have shared with him some of their rituals or tactics, I don't know how well that will transfer into Alpha Phi Alpha or into this evening. These thoughts have crossed my mind beginning last Tuesday.

"Have you told anyone of your affiliation with the Alpha Society?" Gordon asks.

"I have yet to tell anyone." Lemuel responds.

"I actually have spoken to my father about the notion. My father is a historian in Greek studies and found it intriguing to say the least that Negroes in the process of building had chosen Greek letters as their mandate. He is very supportive of our efforts."

"I haven't spoken to anyone either." Gordon states. "Admittedly... too nervous."

I think we are all glad Gordon is so nervous because it affords us a much needed chuckle.

"I wouldn't concern myself so greatly." I try to help. "We will all do fine, do whatever is required and be full members of the Society in a short while."

"For what reason, other than to intimidate us, would we be required to wait in a dimly lit room?" Lemuel asks. The room we have been assigned in the hall is very dark. If the purpose of this room with little light is to petrify, the purposes have been met. At least with Gordon Jones. We were escorted to this room by Mr. Callis, Mr. Kelley and Mr. Tandy as they have instructed us to refer to them as for the evening. Mr. Chapman was present as well but left us before we entered the hall. The remaining three spoke with us in great length and led us to this room to wait. Waiting silently is somewhat difficult in itself, especially when one is awaiting the unknown.

"Did you hear something?" Gordon asks.

Silence fills the room quickly. The other two initiates and I gaze toward the door and throughout the room yet in almost total darkness. Nothing.

"I think your ears are more in tune that usual Gordon." Lemuel says laughing.

"My apologies sirs." Gordon responds.

"No need. Kinckle here is just as nervous as you. He just presents himself better." Lemuel says while laughing and grabbing at my arm in the dark.

Both Gordon and I laugh with him until another sound is heard. This sound is not of Gordon's nervous imagination.

"What was that?" Lemuel whispers.

"I don't know. Whatever it is, it is now closer than the first sound I heard!" Gordon whispers as well.

In an instance, the once darkly dominated room is illuminated by the simple opening of the door. Light chases darkness away in instants too quick to determine by the frail human mind. The silhouette standing in the doorway is none other than Mr. Tandy, betrayed by his shape and the outline of his tall and wide torso.

"Follow me initiates." Mr. Tandy's only spoken words before he turns to lead us away trembling.

"This is a gala event Robert! If I have ever attended one myself!"

"I know you have sweetheart."

"My grandfather would take us every year to a social event in Syracuse. The event is on this order. For the first attempt at a banquet of this magnitude, the Alpha Phi Alpha Society has done extremely well."

I smile at my beautiful wife and agree. The decorations and arrangements are extravagant. I know the committee that worked on the banquet did not have means to work with. The hostess, Mrs. Cohen, has done well in her satisfying of our desire to have an event similar to our White counterparts.

"Robert look at the menu!" Helen says excitedly.

I laugh. "Helen I saw the menu days ago I had a hand in the planning you know."

"Look! Broiled lamb! Shrimp salad! I can't wait!"

"James is an expert. He and Henry were behind much of the culinary planning." I say. I glance toward James who is laughing and speaking with George Kelley. James, originally voted to become an initiate for this evening, was reconsidered and brought in as an old member like George Tompkins.

"Remind me to comment both James and George on the choice of delicacies as well." Helen says.

"I think you are stating that because in your current state, all food is a delicacy!" I say teasingly.

"Robert Harold Ogle!" Helen says slapping my wrist. "You take that back."

I laugh with her as clearly no offense was intended nor taken. "I apologize my love." I kiss my wife's hand.

"Wait until I get you home!" She says jokingly. I laugh with her.

"Good evening Helen... Robert." Nathaniel states approaching. I stand and shake his hand.

"Good evening Nate. Outstanding banquet."

"Yes, and we are only beginning. The speeches are going to electrify. Mine will at least." Nathaniel laughs.

"My Robert is more than prepared. He practiced his speech in front of me and my family."

"Helen, you aren't supposed to expose my secrets! Nate may run into the lavatory to rehearse!" Laughter erupts as George Kelley, the evening's toastmaster begins to quiet the room.

"To the members and guests of the Alpha Phi Alpha Society, we welcome you to our initiatory banquet of 1906."

Light applause fills the room.

"We wish to congratulate and welcome our new initiates, Messr. Lemuel Graves, Messr. Gordon Jones and Messr. Eugene Kinckle Jones."

The applause heightens as the three stand and acknowledge being recognized.

"We look forward to an enjoyable evening of food and well wishes. Please take this time to enjoy our menu as it is now served."

"Robert, make sure you secure my dish. I will return shortly from the ladies room."

"Are you going to rehearse your speech in the mirror?" Helen slaps my arms as she walks away giggling.

"Why organize? I saw in my vision my ancestors who had been in slavery. I saw my father who had escaped from that despicable system and had gone back South as a solder in the Union Army to help subduing of those who held him in bondage. He seemed to encourage me in my determination to help unite our group in a unit."

"Why organize? I stand today on the cusp and the verge of a strong shift in the tide of history. Where a Negro can walk into the annals of the intellectual elite and be considered among the top tenth of the race. While at the same time, within the same history, Colored men swing from trees just a train's ride away."

"I organize for the mandate being placed on each of us. The call being placed squarely on the shoulders of Henry Arthur Callis. The call being placed on Nathaniel Allison Murray. The mangle being handed down to Vertner Woodson Tandy. To everyone in this room, the task is before us."

"We do not owe it to ourselves. Rather, we owe it to individuals in particular. We owe it to the one who has come before and laid the blood stained trail that we can now walk on. We owe it to those following after. The bright young Negro men who will attempt what we attempt and call us sacred for the path we pave for them. We have to organize for both individuals."

"We have our instructions gentlemen. We have our foundation brothers. It has been whispered in our ears and placed before us from long before. It has been sung in hymns and passed in secret. It has been written on our hearts and burns within us. We have seen shining example of the excellence of our endeavors. The spirit within us is thirsting for it."

"What is it? It is the dream that carries each of us on. It is the vision that began with a conversation and culminates in our letters. Every time we gather, we hear it. Every minute we dictate, we listen to it. Our parents have told us. Their parents have told them. Their forefathers spoke it to them. Why organize? So we can dream. So we can carry the dream."

"Dream on, for dreams are sweet. Don't awaken! Dream on, and at thy feet pomegranates shall be shaken. Who likeneth the youth of life to morning? 'Tis the night in truth, rose coloured dreams adorning."

"He's quoting Dunbar! Paul Lawrence Dunbar!" Helen whispers to Robert as he gathers his papers together.

"...sleep, sleep, 'tis sweet to dream. Oh, weep when thou awakes!"

"Thank you."

"Welcome brother. Some may say this herald is specific for Brother Graves, Brother Kinckle Jones and Brother Gordon Jones. For we have duly welcomed them with open arms and open hearts. Yet my call for this evening is for every person who has triumphed and overcome the obstacles to achieve what we have built thus far. My call is to everyone in this room, who has been involved in the Alpha Phi Alpha. Welcome brother."

"The uncertainty that we have faced in the development of the Alpha Phi Alpha group is quickly diminishing and being substituted for the surety of the future. We stand firm in our ideals. What was once unclear and invisible is now becoming clear and filled with purpose. The very acts that we have participated in this evening are the culmination of ideals, discussions and sentiments and a year of meetings. This due diligence has genuinely created in each of us a love for the idea, a love for each other and a brotherly love toward our efforts and toward our members."

"As we look to the horizon of what our intentions may produce, we boldly state that we are brothers forging toward one common resolution the various discussions have been transformed into principles. The conversations have become tenets. The debates have proven to be worthy of encouragement. This evening of gala will become history!"

"As we have opened our doors here, we will continue to open our doors. We will steward the call of our leaders to ensure the safekeeping of Negro men interested in scholarship. We will call them friends and we will call them brothers. For what greater call could we have?"

"I would like to applaud the speakers who have presented before me. Their eloquence has humbled me."

"I stand before you, a young man full of vision and energy. More, a brother of Alpha Phi Alpha with the task of speaking, courage brother."

"It is in these times we must be courageous and unwilling to bend in our task. We face odds that may seem insurmountable yet we know conquerable. The outlawed practice of lynching still exists and rears its ugly head often. As we enjoy the Cornell education, separate but equal goes the road most others of the race travel. As Washington takes to the yard, DuBois calls on the tenth. We are that tenth! We must muster the courage to be, do and carry the task that applies."

"This struggle that we face is unrelenting. This forward climb that we have attached ourselves to is mounting higher. The grounds we have chosen to travel on have yet to be traveled by Colored soles. Yes brotherhood calls us forth and we run heeding the call."

"If we are to become brothers, we have to stand in the face of the ills and declare our time. Frederick Douglass spoke never truer in stating 'Power concedes nothing without a demand; it never has and it never will.' If we choose to look square into the face of the very obstacles that we are mandated to climb over, then climb we must and climb we shall!"

"My brothers, we are now bonded by the inherent call gone forth. We are bonded by the words spoken into the air this evening that have challenged us to continue. Do you see our goal as a finish line or a starting point? I believe that this is the beginning and not the end and we must muster the strength to begin."

"In the same manner in which Henry Callis spoke courage and Bob Ogle spoke welcome, I speak to the same brother to persevere."

"In my goings about Ithaca and about this campus, I've found a myriad of responses to our desire to organize and create a foundation. An older gentleman told me that we cannot hope to do what White folks do. Another student said that by building a fraternity, we would be the laughing stock of the town. While yet another student, a Negro student, informed me that we will go bankrupt after our first big dance! Hearing those statements only has encouraged me and thrust me forward in my desire for Alpha Phi Alpha."

"It is only through God above that we can and will persevere. We must encourage those of our race, both Negro boys and girls to carry the banner and press forward. Each of us has a higher calling to put himself last in place of his brother. For the true spirit to be kindled in each of us is a unique and special gift that we do not lightly take."

"Assume for a moment that each of us is responsible for one Negro boy. What experiences would you share with him? What would you tell him? How would you have him reared? What lessons would you exhort and instill? Having knowledge of all that is around him and what may influence him and what may speak to him in secret, how would you protect him? We must see each other as our own responsibility. We must encourage one another to persevere. It is only the justice that God has granted us for our Alpha Phi Alpha. For after all, what good is Alpha Phi Alpha to any of us if it does not teach us that as a servant of all, we must transcend all through service?"

"I do not place the responsibility on the wheel barrel of others and not to myself. I call out to myself, Nathaniel Allison Murray, to be of reverence to my God first and to be of service and loyalty to my fellow brothers second."

"It is my firm belief that as members of the race, we have an obligation. We not only foster responsibility but also obligation, debt, and loyalty. My subject this evening is loyalty. If brotherhood is our mandate, as was most earnestly spoken of prior, then our underlying principle is loyalty. For how can one profess to being or being received as a brother without some aspect of what loyalty means?"

"There is no question for the need of the entity we have created and developed. Whether that entity be literary or not is not the question. For significantly we have need to understand and study and understand more. Hence the inherent need of literature. To what end will we as brothers and members be once the purpose and foundation is laid?"

"Our commitment need be steadfast and diligent. Our resound unbreakable. The manner in which I pursue endeavors is with the same fortitude. As we have all expressed a sincere level of loyalty one to another, we must continue and permit the foundation to be settled. The layer of loyalty underneath the surface of brotherhood."

"As chair of the committee on initiations, I also welcome and commend Brother Jones, Brother Jones and Brother Graves. As you have shown diligence and consistency in your endeavors for membership, we shall show the same level of diligence in our quest for brotherhood toward you. I do nothing more than echo what the previous speakers have stated as to your new membership and welcome."

"Since becoming associated with the gentlemen in this room under the direct supervision of Professor Poindexter, I have learned much. I have considered myself responsible to a significant degree to the carrying out of the mandates we have established. More because I have seen more, done more, and experienced more. Yet know less because I am unfamiliar with any entity quite like what we are embarking. I thank you gentlemen for this experience and this opportunity. It is my sincere belief that we will strive forward with a true sense and spirit of loyalty for each other and for Alpha Phi Alpha for the benefit of all that come."

"So who do you feel has given the greatest speech thus far?"

"Robert Harold Ogle!" Helen says smiling.

"You're teasing... yet I agree." Helen and I laugh.

"Who speaks next? Vertner?"

"Professor Poindexter. Vertner is not speaking this evening."

"To the distinguished gentlemen of the Alpha Phi Alpha Society, I bid you fond greetings and wishes. My speech is on the topic, ideals."

"What are the ideals of any great society? What are the ideals of this Society? What will be heralded as the foundation of this organization and its principles? If we are its founding fathers, what will be said of us? Who would have led to success through our endeavors?"

"When we began our correspondence, the idea that kindled in our hearts began to burn brightly and tremendous visions were brought forth. The fascinating aspect for me is that the very idea had been dormant in my mind from semesters past. I had not received such support until the semester of the fall 1905. The idea of a literary society that would cultivate the minds of Negro students, promote and excel in educational endeavors, create functions of cultural significance to the surrounding community, and bond the far and few between students of Color on campus has occupied my thoughts on several occasions. With this loyal band of students, the idea has been realized."

"True to the form of what we began a little more than one year ago, we maintain the ability to teach and mentor Negro students and provide a true academic fortress for them. Nothing has propelled our race as has reading and education and that is our ideal. Frederick Douglass came into contact with the writer William Lloyd Garrison after reading him in the Liberator. Afterward, Douglass said that Garrison's work took its place with him next to the Bible. Oh how that manuscript changed the course of history through Frederick Douglass!"

"What we have achieved is monumental and I do not

take credit as one who has led the charge and been so instrumental in what has become. I more press upon ourselves the importance of remaining steadfast to our ideals and purposes. What good, as someone else mentioned, is Alpha Phi Alpha Society if we do not cater to the very call?"

"The course of study has been set for the upcoming year. The reading material is available and well within our reach. The archives have been built, consisting of a tremendous amount of stored information to assist Negro students that follow you. Do not abandon the straightway path set."

"Thank you, each of you. Please enjoy the remainder of your evening."

The banquet was a grand affair. The menu was spectacular and the overall sentiment is one that will rest in our spirits for a time to come. Each brother left with a renewed sense of purpose and a will to earnestly pursue that which beckons us.

If anything, it seems most difficult to resolve the issue which has beset us from the beginning. The strife between those for the literary society and those for the fraternity. With this two edged sentiment still very much alive, the direction and pursuit of purpose remains tainted.

"Great job on your speech Henry."

"Thank you Bob. Yours' was well received."

"Thank you sir Helen enjoyed herself immensely. Especially the lady fingers." Robert and I laugh."

"That is good to know!" I say.

C.C. Poindexter enters the room and begins the meeting without much salutation or greeting. "Gentlemen, I have received a request from Rev. Auten of the Zion Church that we give an entertainment function at his church after Thanksgiving."

"An entertainment function?" George Kelley asks. "What type of entertainment?

"We will read and give oratorical. I was impressed with the presentation at the banquet and want to continue in the same light. "C.C. responds. "That is one of the tasks of a literary society. Since that is what capacity we occupy, that is what we will do."

"In that sense, I don't suggest we do it." George Kelley states.

"Pardon?"

"It is clear that the sentiment is shifting from brothers in this room away from literary organization."

As George Kelley steps forward and speaks for everyone, he initiates a heated verbal debate with Professor Poindexter. One the likes of which none in the room would like to participate.

"I move we lay this topic on the table for discussion at a later date." Nathaniel wisely moves that the issue be resolved for the moment by postponing.

"I second the motion." I say quickly.

I quickly noticed C.C. glance toward George Tompkins before the vote is taken. As those in favor are counted versus those against, a tie results. C.C. casting the deciding vote, the motion dies.

George Tompkins quickly moves. "I move we provide an entertainment for the Zion Church after Thanksgiving."

This vote results in a tie as the vote prior. With C.C. as the deciding, this motion carries. We are now responsible for entertainment at the church.

"Thank you gentlemen." C.C. states with a clear level of satisfaction. "I have compiled reading material that we can research to choose what our presentation will consist of."

"I move for the appointment of a committee to design an Alpha Phi Alpha pin." George Kelley states confidently. This motion is clearly an item that George has had on his mind. Either as a suggestion from the Theta Beta boys from their jacket insignia or the large crest within their house or something that George has personally wanted for us. A fraternity emblem seals our endeavors clearly. There is no question as to the meaning behind an organization such as ours with its own pin.

"I second the motion!" Vertner excitedly blurts out.

"I third the motion!" Eugene says to the laughter of the rest. Not surprising to me, C.C. finds no humor.

When the vote is tallied, a surprising result has happened. The vote is overwhelmingly in favor of a pin design. This is the largest one sided vote we have yet to witness as the fraternal idea has never been as strong as is now expressed in this vote. George beams with a level of satisfaction he has yet to express. This is a clear victory to any of us who have secretly had the desire for Alpha Phi Alpha to emerge as a fraternity. The first fraternity of its kind as it is started by an all Colored band of students. Monumental in itself is the mere thought.

"I move the committee consist of Brother George Kelley and Brother Vertner. Vertner did an outstanding piece of work on the bulletins for the banquet. I think his architecture background has extended itself into other areas of artwork."

"Indeed!" Vertner proclaims proudly. "I would be honored and proudly work diligently to represent our efforts as best possible in a pin design."

"I accept as well as I have already begun with plans and ideas as to how I would like to see the pin displayed and worn." George adds.

"I think a pin is an outstanding idea and proposal for us at this stage." James says. "It is not only timely, but well calculated. I would display proudly."

As I glance around the room of brothers who I have grown to bond with either over the last year or the last few months, I begin to understand the magnitude of what we have embarked upon. Talk amongst one another escalates as George Kelley's suggestion has excited almost everyone in the room. The new initiate Gordon speaks to Vertner excitedly about pin ideas. Eugene has ideas I'm sure. George humbly yet confidently gloats over the victory of the vote. Amidst this all is our presiding officer Professor C.C. Poindexter. This minor defeat has taken more of its toll on him the loser than it has on the spirits of the winner. C.C. seems to have a difficult time in regaining order in the meeting. A position I have never seen for C.C. He has lost the very fire that he spoke of just days earlier in his presentation at our initiation banquet.

Working alongside a man of Poindexter's caliber, mind and diligence lends me to understand his character a bit more than the others. I am as impressed with his resolve as I am with a George Kelley or a Nathaniel or a Robert. Each in his own right of tremendous character and persistence. Who could imagine the burden carried by a Robert Harold Ogle with a young wife and first baby on the way while just a sophomore in college? Yet he plans and debates and stands fast on the mission to build a lasting legacy within Alpha Phi Alpha no less than anyone else. Never missing a meeting, never losing an opportunity for battle, always fast to reconciliation, and always fast for a smile. C.C. invokes the same impressiveness as he presents himself strong, this is my first time seeing C.C. weak.

Tonight's meeting concludes with a level of excitement we had yet to experience to this point. I don't feel just from the mention of the pin or any particular fraternal emblem. Much more the tide of the spirit. As long as the time had been coming, it seems to have arrived. With it, a spirit unlike any we have seen.

"It's been over thirty minutes. Neither C.C. nor Henry are here." Vertner says to me.

"It's neither like Poindexter to be late nor the punctual Callis," I respond.

"George, be prepared nonetheless to chair the meeting in the event that neither arrive."

As Vertner gives me these instructions, Henry enters the house.

"Henry, we've all been awaiting both you and Professor

Poindexter." Gordon says.

"I apologize for my tardiness but I bring news from Professor Poindexter." Henry says as he removes his overcoat.

"I call the meeting to order then to hear what you have to present." Everyone takes his chair and focuses his attention on Henry.

"I received a letter from Professor Poindexter. I have been instructed to read in the presence of the rest of the members of the Society." Henry states as he opens an envelope and unfolds a letter. He tucks the envelope away and begins to read C.C.'s words. "This is what it says: 'To the members of the Alpha Phi Alpha Society, it is with my deep regret that I have chosen to resign as the presiding officer of the Society.'" Henry pauses before continuing. "'I cannot place myself in which the Negro has not a place nor a heritage the collegiate fraternal system is.'"

"Read that part again Henry." I say.

Henry looks up at me, then back to the letter. "'I cannot place myself in which the Negro has not a place nor a heritage the collegiate fraternal system is.' I don't quite understand it but there is more."

"Please continue."

"'The aspirations that I had for the literary society are lost as you endeavor and pursue this idea of fraternity, as this notion has no place in the heart of the Colored student, it has no place in my heart either. I cannot associate myself with the resemblance of any such institution. Good luck to you in your future endeavors. Professor Charles C. Poindexter, College of Agriculture, Cornell University.' That is the end of the letter."

"What is the meaning of the section that you read?" Nathaniel asks.

"It seems very unclear. I don't know. Especially for a wordsmith like Professor Poindexter."

"Clearly it is a resignation letter." I state.

"Yes it is." Henry responds.

"I move," George Tompkins says, "that we make a sincere effort to communicate with C.C.... Professor Poindexter... to gain a clearer understanding of his statement and reasons for this action."

There is a moment of silence as I am sure most, like myself, do not know how to respond to Tompkins' motion.

"I second." Henry avails.

As I call for the vote, it carries. However, the mood in the room has changed significantly and it becomes even difficult to move to the next item of old business. C.C. Poindexter has resigned as presiding officer! This is a tremendous loss yet an incredible opportunity as a stepping stone for the fraternal advancement.

As we move through the items on Henry's agenda, the thought exists clear in each mind in the room. How do we proceed now without C.C. at the helm?

"Gentlemen, if I make a general statement," Charles says, "I feel that we have come into a new existence in Alpha Phi Alpha. If indeed we are without C.C. Poindexter, then we can embark upon a new direction with all diligence."

"I agree." Eugene says. "I admire and respect Professor Poindexter for his leadership ability. Yet I have wanted deeply to express my desire for the Society to become a fraternity. It is something that has been on my heart since I set foot on this campus and met you brothers. I was amazed at what had been accomplished in just one short year. I cherish the call placed forth inviting me to such a significant role."

"It is something I dare say I have wanted as well." Vertner states. "In my mind, the very concept of a Negro based fraternity is exceptional. I took careful concern in drawing up a pin reflective of our Greek letters. As careful and as honest as I created the design for the banquet. I am in full favor of the fraternity and have been since months prior."

Robert stands to make his statement. "If we hold true to the very things we have said in our statements on the 30th, then it is clear where we stand. We have spoken of opposition and obstacles. No one dare call by name, yet we all recognize the sentiment and spirit that has existed. One for literary club and one for secret fraternity. Yet the latter has been leaned toward more lately. I have always championed the cause of fraternity as has been consistent with my vote. I stand in the very position, unchanged now."

"Fellows," Henry begins, "I admire C.C. a great deal. The interactions that he and I have had have been moving. I have seen the disappointment in his demeanor as we have made decision after decision, pushing us more toward the fraternal concept. Yet we cannot back away from this calling and what may lie ahead. I believe we have the opportunity to change the course of history. What we have within our grasp is special and unique and worthy of embracing by every male student of the race. The talented tenth that come through the hallways of Cornell. With both vision and boldness we forge ahead. Claiming what we have all dreamed of at one time or another. Some of us have been guilty of voting on either issue. Maybe to appease or maybe out of sincerity. This day, Tuesday December 4th can mark a monumental day in the life of Alpha Phi Alpha. At least in what it can become. It can be monumental if we are first true to ourselves and true to our brothers, one another."

"I have always been in favor of Alpha Phi Alpha Fraternity. I have gathered much information from my friends at Theta Beta Pi and have thought of nothing else but to implement some of it, altering it of course, but making it our own. My resolve toward this end has been tremendous as I have felt the strong will to complete what was first presented to us over one year ago. Now is our time and now is our moment. Like Robert has stated, most of us spoke on the very obstacles that were placed in our way. Each one we have debated through, argued through, or climbed over. There are seemingly none left standing. All that remain is the brotherhood, the one lasting element of a true spirit of fraternity."

"Brothers," Nathaniel states, "never have I been so pleased to follow Roberts' Rules of Order!" Everyone laughs. "I move that we express a decision upon Alpha Phi Alpha to either continue with the idea of becoming a fraternity or continue as an organization for mutual benefit. The time has come and a decision has to be made."

This is clearly the most important decision we have ever made as an entity. This is the decisive moment in which some of us or all of us have envisioned. Never before has such liberty entered into our midst as each person carefully considers which way they will honestly vote. If the fraternal side dies in this vote it is very likely that the notion won't exist. Had it not been for the strong opposition of C.C. Poindexter, this motion may have carried, in sentiment at least, much prior to this date. With C.C.'s resignation in hand, the members of this Society have the freedom to vote however they please without any consequence. If this does not foster the emergence of our fraternity, I don't believe anything will.

I glance toward Henry first, then Nathaniel; proponents of the Alpha Phi Alpha Fraternity. Gentlemen that I have learned to call brother because of the endless nights we have spent in meeting over the last fourteen months. Men who I have learned to respect and admire.

I look at Eugene Jones who only having met a few short months ago has left a definite impression on me unlike anyone I have ever met.

I remember when Charles and I spoke about the idea of the fraternity over lunch. His sharp mind and business acclimate are a strong indication of what type of fraternity member he would be.

Seated next to Robert, I place my hand on his shoulder in a congratulatory way. I know him from individual conversations that he and I have had that this is a moment he has awaited. His smile back at me is all the assurance I was looking for.

Vertner takes off his glasses, wipes his forehead, and readjusts. He notices me looking at him and smiles his familiar and jovial smile. Seeing me seated in the position of Chair, he knows that this could very well be the most significate vote Alpha Phi Alpha has ever taken. I don't believe he will take this lightly.

The vote is taken and by majority decision, we have become Alpha Phi Alpha Fraternity."

"I move," Nathaniel states, "that a committee is organized right away in order to institute the organization of the fraternity and fraternal matters."

"I second." Lemuel says proudly.

"I move that the committee on the fraternal organization consist of Brothers Callis, Morton, Eugene Jones, Murray and myself." Charles moves. His motion carries.

"Gentlemen," George Tompkins stands and takes up his coat. "I cannot belong to a fraternity. I officially and formally resign. I wish to have no more correspondence with Alpha Phi

Alpha."

Henry's attempt to persuade George Tompkins to reconsider is futile. As George prepares to leave, Nathaniel moves that we accept George Tompkins' resignation with regret. The motion carries.

For the first time since September 1905, everyone in attendance is of one mind and one accord, now members of Alpha Phi Alpha Fraternity. As the meeting adjourns, we greet one another like never before. Now we are fraternity brothers. Now we are bonded together by a mission and an oath. Now we are founders in a great sense to an organization that may benefit hundreds of Negro students that come after us. Finally we have realized our dream, to one day look at one another wearing the letters A Phi A and understand the meaning, the courage, and the perseverance it took to establish the first college fraternity for Negro men.

Letters to the Fraternity from the Jewels

To the General President and the brothers of Alpha Phi Alpha Fraternity, Incorporated,

I bid you a fond greeting! How remarkable it is that the fraternity has reached and surpassed its Centennial celebration! As the spirit and legacy of Alpha Phi Alpha and its founders lives on, I, Brother Henry Arthur Callis commend each brother who has embraced the spirit and forged ahead.

Alpha Phi Alpha has at its genesis forethought, vision, hard work and tenacity placed against a backdrop of lynchings, racism, classism and miseducation. Yet we have seen the fraternity grow and embrace thousands of brothers who have triumphed and successfully navigated through these 100 years. Speaking on behalf of each founder, I thank you.

As we as an organization prepare to turn the next page in our ever growing history, we must address the concerns of African Americans to an even greater extent. I have always been of the mindset that if every man who has accepted the challenge to become an Alpha man does his part within his chapter, then we have the strength in numbers to eradicate any ill will we choose to overcome. The decision is each one of ours to make. Imagine what we could do for America's homeless population if every Alpha man donated one dollar? Our strength is tremendous brothers; steer it positive.

As I have watched and admired great men enter the hallowed halls of Alpha men much greater in terms of accomplishments that I, I have been awed by their capacity at leadership. The characteristic portrayal of an Alpha man is a dedicated leader, a trustworthy brother, and an honest friend. Some of the brothers, much too many to name, I have met in my travels epitomize this very synopsis. I have had the pleasure of singing the fraternal hymn with many of you brothers and I thank you graciously for the experience.

Looking back on our 100 year history, do not lean on the past to dictate what the future should be. Forge and create your own destiny. We have made mistakes along the way. There are problems in some chapters that none of the founders or good men of Alpha are proud of. Move from those items and change. Encourage young brothers to reach and achieve for scholastic excellence and brotherhood. Respect older brothers for their wisdom and perseverance. Graduate brothers, guide and lead collegiate brothers. College brothers, make impacts on your campuses and in your communities. Let service be each one's call to duty. Wear Alpha Phi Alpha with pride and dignity for it was established with pride and dignity. Lastly, embrace the same spirit and aims; manly deeds, scholarship, and love for all mankind that drove a young Henry, Charles, Eugene, George, Nathaniel, Robert and Vertner to found this great fraternity.

Henry Arthur Callis, MD
Founder

My dear brothers of Alpha Phi Alpha Fraternity,

It is with great pleasure that I address you. As I look at the long list of accomplishments that have been heralded by the various brothers of the fraternity, one cannot help but admire the extreme sense of diligence and service the brotherhood has undertaken.

None of your founders quite comprehended the magnitude of our various meetings in fall 1905 and subsequent semesters. Our undying spirit has yet to be quenched and we trust it will never be. As Alpha Phi Alpha moves toward even higher heights, look forward to the good you can do for one another.

My challenge to each individual considering his own position and status is to evaluate the difference you can make. There are young men in need of mentorship, a brother figure, or a sound shoulder to lean on. That is what your founders were to one another. That is what every Alpha Phi Alpha brother need be.

Brothers, work hard to maintain the high standard that is Alpha Phi Alpha.

To the leadership of this great organization, stand in the stead of us your Jewel founders. The awesome task is upon you to create new history each day.

Fraternally and sincerely,
C.H. Chapman
Founder

Brothers, It is with a sense of pride that I, your Jewel founder, address you. To recognize that the hard fought labor that the founders and associating brothers went through to secure a fraternal home for generations to come has been kept in order is a glorious tribute. When I stepped foot on the grounds of Cornell University in September 1906, I could not fathom that my actions would have such a wide affect and reach so many. Yet it is with great determination that your founders moved beyond the gates of Ithaca and Cornell and into the vast collegiate world. With the same determined mind and set spirit must you endeavor to change the lives of all you come into contact with as men of Alpha.

It was once said about me that I performed human acts of kindness for others rather than having others serve me. This is the heart of Alpha Phi Alpha; service to humanity and love for all mankind. As I chose my various endeavors in life, nothing short of this mandate drove me onward.

I have been ever so fortunate to dine with dignitaries and travel extensively. I have represented Alpha Phi Alpha in many areas of Europe as well as across America from coast to coast. I am the only Jewel founder with the distinction of a father who is a member of Alpha Phi Alpha. I also am proud of my son Eugene Jr. who is a brother of Alpha Phi Alpha. The fraternity has been a great aid and a badge of honor in all my life's accomplishments.

I have set my course on the underprivileged and downtrodden. Much of my life's work has been to raise a level of social conscious for African Americans and men in particular. Many are familiar with my work and dedication to the National Urban League. It is this vehicle that I found comfort and purpose. Through the efforts of the League and my association with A Phi, numerous lives are reformed. The fraternity has always taken an active role in support of the League and it is more than encouraging knowing that the leadership of the League is now in the capable hands of a brother of Alpha Phi Alpha.

When Art Callis and I spent tireless hours with the name of our beloved fraternity, it was with a great measure of concern that we took to indoctrinate purpose and definition. Witnessing the centennial transition of this great body of brothers and now the years beyond, justifies our efforts. I can rest in the belief that this spirit will travel forward and continue to grow far and wide. As our fraternity accepts the mandate of a new day, a new era, and a greater purpose, we must each embrace this greater purpose and live it every day. It was this purpose that propelled Vertner Tandy and I to form Beta chapter, Gamma chapter and Alpha Lambda chapter. It is with this desire that you must now forge new roads to pioneer yourselves.

The task is yours' brothers. Do well in the name of A Phi and the Jewels.

Fraternally,
Jewel Eugene Kinckle Jones

'I said to a man who stood at the gate of the year; Give me a light that I may tread safely into the unknown.' and he replied, 'Go out into the darkness and put your hand into the hand of God. That shall be to you better than a light and safer than a known way.' I recited those very words at our anniversary convention 50 years ago. I am delighted to know that after 50 additional years plus some, Alpha Phi Alpha Fraternity still stands and is a pillar in communities around this nation.

At the same time brothers, we must revisit the purpose behind Alpha Phi Alpha. There was once a time where members of the surrounding community would call upon the Alpha men for assistance. There were very supportive members of the Ithaca community when your founders were students at Cornell. The community relied on Alpha Phi Alpha when it came to matters of civil and human rights. Yet it seems that the very community that once celebrated us now holds conversations of hazing, lewd behavior and other subjects unbecoming of any brother of this fraternity. There are stories of men being brutally beaten in order to gain access to the fraternity. There are chapters reporting low attendance at every service event yet high attendance at social functions and dances. Brothers this is not our mandate.

The seven founders of this fraternity sought a bond of brotherhood. Our ideals and vision were for a fraternity of loyal brothers will allegiance to God, family and country. Also a love for the brotherhood that has secured him to the motto. This organization has for over 100 years stood for these principles and these mandates must be adhered to. As the first General President of this fraternity, I implore that this be the rally cry from each brother in a leadership capacity from the General President to the board members, to the regional officers, to the chapter presidents, to the conference delegates. Each brother upholding the high standards of Alpha Phi Alpha along the way.

Brothers, remember that Alpha Phi Alpha is a symbol for what men should be. Men should be held accountable for their actions and responsible for their very endeavors. Alpha Phi Alpha is not a badge that one can put on and take off at his leisure. Alpha Phi Alpha is not a club for one to look forward to receiving a letterman's jacket or shirt. Realize you are representing Alpha Phi Alpha every time you speak. With every act of service or disservice you do, you are working on the behalf of the founders of the fraternity. In every instance that you are to act outside of the characteristic of a true Alpha man, think twice for you represent much more than yourself Brother.

I am proud to be a founder of this great organization. I commend the brothers who have worked tirelessly to keep our dream alive. I honor the Alpha men that have made headway in the fields of science, politics and medicine. There are tremendous efforts made by Alpha brothers in athletics, education and the fine arts. I look on with pride at the many Alphas that are in the military, in social services, are entrepreneurs, or behind pulpits in churches all over the world. It is my sincere wish to encourage and admonish you brothers to continue in the name of Alpha Phi Alpha.

In closing brother, remember what you speak when you pass on the oral and written history of this fraternity. As you cultivate the minds of young African American male students, remember the future General President of Alpha Phi Alpha may be in your midst as could be the future President of the United States. We have the potential brothers. We, your Jewel founders, had it and we have left it for you. Embrace it! Take it! Live out the spirit of Alpha Phi Alpha!

Fraternally yours,
Jewel George Biddle Kelley

Brother President, Board of Directors, and the current body of brothers of Alpha Phi Alpha,

Do all you can for dear old Alpha Phi Alpha! I open my fraternal address with the slogan that led us forth and held us together shortly after our founding year of 1906. Do all you can for dear old Alpha Phi Alpha!

In the fall of 1905, like-minded students came together to unite under a common banner on the grounds of Cornell University. With only purpose as our beacon of guiding light, we marched through quite unknowingly as to what we were essentially accomplishing. As the picture became clear, the evidence of our labor became apparent and Alpha Phi Alpha Fraternity was born on December 4th, 1906.

Since its inception, Alpha Phi Alpha has been a major contributor to the social, economic, and political uplift of the African American race. I am proud to know that there have been accomplishments made by brothers of this fraternity such as Brother W.E.B. DuBois, Brother Alonzo Herndon, Brother Charles H. Wesley, Brother Mal Goode, Brother Dr. Martin Luther King Jr., Brother Jessie Owens, Brother Countee Cullen, Brother Thurgood Marshall, Brother Adam Clayton Powell Jr., Brother Duke Ellington, Brother Andrew Young, Brother Paul Robeson and many more. There are so many that I could never name in one address. Yet there are such hills to climb and such worthy brothers to recognize that have yet to take their position in the struggle. Grab hold to what has been laid before you Brother and pull your load.

Hundreds of Negroes are still skeptical of Black genius. I made that claim in 1936 at the 30th Anniversary Convention and this skepticism holds even truer at our 100th anniversary and beyond. What set of shoulders is the blame placed on for this intent? On those who carry the skepticism or on those who have the potential of genius but never express it to defy the former? Brothers, hear me when I mentioned that it is not this body of brothers that I address that need the proverbial awakening but the thousands of young men we are charged to mentor to help draw their genius potential. If someone had not mentored you, where would you be? If someone had not mentored me, where would I be? If someone had not mentored me, where would Alpha Phi Alpha be? More than that, if someone had not mentored you, where would Alpha

Phi Alpha be?

Lay claim to the call and make it your own. Make it your chapters'. Make it your fraternities'. Congratulations Alpha Phi Alpha on over 100 years and what the good Lord will bring you in the next century.

Fraternally yours,
N. A. Murray, Jewel

To my brothers of Alpha Phi Alpha Fraternity Incorporated,

As many of you look back on the number of years you have been a part of this illustrious organization, I congratulate you. Every member need reminisce his journey into this great bond of brotherhood. As well, please allow me, your Jewel Fonder, the same courtesy as I travel my personal road into Alpha Phi Alpha.

Along with six of my closest comrades, men who were once unacquainted, we founded the greatest organization founded for African American men. Between the years of 1905 and 1906, we saw our attempts at a literary society and book club evolve into a fraternity so strong, so vast and so wide that it would cover colleges and universities around the world. Your Jewel founders evolved to become established men in their fields and well respected members of our fraternity. We maintained and held closely the mandates we established at Cornell and kept those ideals close to our hearts. We established a vehicle that not only stood for the betterment of African American men but of the surrounding community as well.

In my recollection of these years, I can say that this fraternity exemplifies what true brotherhood and manly deeds are. When a brother is at his weakest, it is when other brothers stand strong. When a brother is at his strongest, it is then when he shares his strength with his brothers. I became a brother on December 4th, 1906. I became my weakest when I became a widower on October 3rd, 1908. In all times and in all circumstances, the call to brotherhood has carried me on and through.

As we set our course to embark upon these next 100 years, stand in the place of us, your Jewel founders. Forge through areas never yet journeyed. Let Alpha shine in all endeavors. Let every son of Alpha express loyalty and fraternity in all that we set our hearts to do. Rededicate yourselves to Alpha Phi Alpha.

In closing brothers, I would like to quote the words of my favorite brother and the most eloquent Alpha that I know, 'In spite of the length of life of the fraternity, that in order to keep that life going and to improve leadership among our folk in America, Alpha Phi Alpha will have to utilize her brains, in planning for excellence in public relations.' Jewel Henry Arthur Callis was never so correct in his assessment! Be strong, consistent and unimpeachable brothers.

Thank you and fraternal always,

Robert H. Ogle

Founder

To the most noble brothers of the Alpha Phi Alpha Fraternity.

I greet you in this year of our Lord and in the 100 surplus years of our beloved fraternity.

Now with the formalities aside and the generalities made, let me converse as the Vertner that some may know me as. As Jewel founder of this great body of brothers, I am probably best known for my accomplishments after my time at Cornell. The field of architecture was good to me in that it afforded me notoriety and much acclaim. By designing for such members of society as Madam CJ Walker ad some of the leading congregations in Harlem, NY, I was able to become one of the leading architects within the race.

How many know the Vertner before Cornell? How many brothers know enough about the history of the organization to tell me something about myself? Do you respect and understand the legacy and history behind this organization or are you thrilled to be able to attend a dance with fraternity brothers? Have you aligned yourself with the founders, the first initiates, the first chapters and the ideals of this fraternity? Or have you chosen to follow the hoodlums that have A Phi A on their hats? I use the term hoodlum lightly my brothers yet not in jest. I have heard stories of young men desiring Alpha Phi Alpha and been beaten until they bled or couldn't walk. I have heard stories of mild concussions from blows to the head by blunt objects. This is not what Alpha Phi Alpha was founded for, nor did your Jewel founders work so hard to achieve so little.

Instead, those brothers who have heeded the call and found themselves true to the underlying purpose of Alpha Phi Alpha Fraternity need rise and lead the way. Let there be more news of the triumphant achievements Alpha men are known for. Alpha men tend to excel in all endeavors of campus life and community development. Let that be our banner, not the former.

We have to change as an organization and keep the minds of all seven of the founders as our focus in moving ahead. A very wise brother once stated, 'Recognition and remedy of defects is not only desirable but mandatory lest we repeat...' Do you know what famous brother lays claim to that statement? Me! Jewel Vertner Woodson Tandy! Founding father of Alpha Phi Alpha Fraternity!

Fraternally yours,
V.W. Tandy
Jewel Founder

Thank You

Thank You Father God for the gift of writing; a skill You have deposited into me without me earning it or deserving it. I love you Lord, thank You. Thank You Jesus for saving my soul. Thank You Holy Spirit for speaking to me, guiding me and helping me to write this book. I wish to thank the seven Jewels of this great fraternity for founding an organization that has changed the world. Thank you to the brothers of Beta chapter that saw fit to vote me in by the skin of my teeth. Thank you to my Dean Jaret C. Riddick, my assistant deans Darryl Arnold and William A. Green III, and my line brothers, the spring 1990 line, the Heirs of Hermakis; R. Tim Gibbs, Charles Graham, Dr. L. Steve Vaughan, Richard Chiles, Brian Jackson, Rickey Green, Mareco Edwards, Ronald Sullivan, Scott Edwards, Carl Martin, Jolm Adams, Darnell VanRensalier, Keith Perry, Cliff Floyd, and Arnold Jolivet II. I want to thank my spec family, William Brown, Marc Gay, James Young, Donnie Hoskey, Warren Irons, Brandon Neal, Ryan Ridley, Dr. Jaha Howard, Armond Mosley, Dr. Kareem Merrick, Jamar Dowdy, Bobby Cabbagestalk, Adam Cooper and Clarence James. You brothers are doing incredible things, continue to hold the light of Alpha high! I want to thank my fraternity brother, best friend, business partner and brother in the Lord Paul Woodruff, the best graphic designer in the world. PPPPPP! Thank you for your friendship, accountability, creativity and brotherly love! I wish to thank my fraternity brothers C. Brian Williams; my good friend and the Executive Director of Step Afrika! and my fraternity brother and good friend, Rev. Brian McCollum. You both are the epitome of what Alpha men are and should be! Thank you for your friendship, laughs and brotherhood. To all of the brothers of Alpha who have performed with me in Step Afrika! – Steve, Brett, Sean, Lion, Ben, Jamel, Dave, OJ, Kiragu, Will, Jakari, Delonte, Chris, and Joe. Thank you for all the hand claps, foot taps and Zulu kicks! I want to thank the brothers Omicron Lambda Alpha chapter and I particular, three distinguished leaders – Past President Denny Johnson, Past President Levonia Wiggins and Brother Leon Gordon. Thank you for your leadership and direction over the years. I want to thank Jeff Johnson who is one of the most brotherly Alphas I have ever met and continues to work hard in community service and upholding the name of Alpha Phi Alpha. I wish to thank Brother Lawrence Ware who has advised me on this book and has taken the journey with me from start to finish. I wish to thank Brother Herman "Skip" Mason for your sound advice and nuggets of information about our seven Jewels. I wish to thank Brother Jason Jurkowski for your constant brotherly love and for the true spirit of the fraternity which you have in your heart. I wish to thank Brother William Lyle, the Executive Director of Alpha Phi Alpha. You have always been a good friend. Thank you for all of your help. I want to thank Brother Elvin Dowling who has come through for me and this project in an enormous way. I cannot thank you enough. I wish to thank each brother who provided me a tagline for this book, especially those on short notice. I wish to thank General President Harry Johnson, General President Darryl Matthews and General President Mark Tillman for your taglines which have been attached to the Jewels novels. To all the Alphas that I know and have grown to admire and be honored to call brother, you are far too many to name but I appreciate you all! Keep holding up the light of A Phi A high! I wish to acknowledge and thank Leona Willis, my good friend from Howard University who helped me navigate the reading and writing of this book. Thanks to my friend/soror/number Carmen Davis for all of your help with the historical resources. Thanks to my photographer Bobby Shanklin who was ready, willing and able to provide the cover photography for the first book. Thanks to my brothers who posed for the cover for the first book; Brother Chris Carter, Brother Earl Fitzhugh, Brother Nicholas Gourdine, Brother James Harmon, Brother Robert Jones, Brother Ronnie Lewis and Brother Terrence Tarver. Thanks bros for showing up ready and on such short notice. Just like Alpha men, always prepared! Thank you to Brother Phil John who cast the brothers who posed for the Second Edition book cover and also posed as one of the Jewels. You are the epitome of operating in excellence and I thank you sincerely. Thank you to Brother James Ravenell who photographed the brothers for the cover and also posed as one of the Jewels. Thank you to the brothers who posed as the Jewels; Brother Roger Manzanarez, Brother Jabari Gray, Brother Shawn Curwen, Brother Joseph L. Sessum, and Brother Jerry Barrow. Thank you to Amina Brown, my very talented graphic designer for designing some of the promotional products for the Jewels First Edition. Thank you to Brother Jossan Robinson for designing the cover and promotional materials for the Jewels Second Edition. Both of you are awesome designers and I thank you! Thank you to Norman Rich, my business partner and graphic designer who assisted with the website and book layout for the Second Edition. I want to thank all of my friends who volunteer and help me sell books as a vendor at the various conventions that I attend. You are the best friends an author could have and I thank you! I want to thank my parents James and Bertha Gourdine for standing behind me in all that I set my mind to, as crazy as my ideas sound at times. To my brother Darnell and his family, Timika, Zarria and Jackson and my sister Stephanie, thank you for your love and support. Thank you to my cousin Jason Gourdine who shot, edited and produced the promotional video on the Jewels website (www.jewels1906.com). You are an extremely talented young man and I can't wait to develop major projects with you! A big thank you to all the fans of As the Sands Burn, Beyond the Burning Sands, and The Saved and The Restless. It has been your support over the years that has kept me writing and has encouraged me to continue on. If it had not been for the loyal fans that follow my work, this book could not have been possible. Thank you to each of you. The biggest thank you goes to my wife, Kathy, who puts up with me sitting at my laptop in the wee hours of the morning and the late hours of the night. Thank you so much! Thank you to my son, Dylan, who sits on my lap as I write. I write and pour out my gift for you buddy! I love you both! Last but certainly not least, I want to thank you... the person holding this book and reading it right now. I hope you have been blessed by this true account of some truly amazing African American students that changed the course of college life forever. As you close this book, remember one thing from their lives... if God could do it for them, He can do it for you and I as well!

God bless you richly and mightily!
Darrius Jerome Gourdine

Made in the USA
Columbia, SC
22 June 2023

18554200R00114